Y0-CAS-613

At six months old, having my first studio session.

At two months old and just arrived at home, dark as dark chocolate.

Mimi and Aba keep very few pictures of me sleeping in my pen.

Two-year-old birthday party—stealing a first bite of cake before sharing it with five canine guests and three resident toy poodles, the latter put on Public Relations duty at the Dog Café by their "mother".

In costume: tails of grey silk with black lapels, white shirt front and black bow tie, which I wore again on Valentine's Day 2009.

My second studio session in May 2008 turned out to be a happy family reunion!

I admit to a little vanity and weakness for the Peak piazza, an outdoor photo studio where I've grown accustomed to being asked to pose for snap-shots.

"This is a puppy full of God's grace!"

Pets Benediction Sunday at the Cathedral, where I received the Vicar General's blessing, introduced by Mimi as, "a great cohesive force in our family".

The SPCA Fun Day at Christmas 2008 at Dogs' Park, when Bobby was second in the obstacle race, and I ended up co-third with Bean Bean.

At the walkathon at Tai Tam Country Park, November 2008, that TV star and that pop singer gave me the talent contest first prize: a pet pram.

After the obstacle race, more (and freer, hence greater) fun with Bean Bean.

At home, with Chinese New Year decorations and my look-alike chew toy.

With a background of palm trees and sunny beach, couldn't help kissing… (Guess who?)

Aba in a Burberry shirt to catch up with my change of costume.

Turned tails.

Phoebus, in polo shirt and jeans, borrowed a dog's bow tie and wore it to match my formal dress.

Studio Paradiso (which sadly has now ceased operation).

There was a snow-capped mountain against which I rode in a colourful toy convertible buggy.

Chocolate's Brown Study in the Bag

Aba willingly serves as my prop for obstacle race practice.

"The way Chocolate runs, fore and hind legs alternately off the ground, ears and tail thrown up in the air—that's a beautiful picture of pure happiness!"

Ha ha ha! I am having a ball—I mean happy with my ball.

They play fetch with me, throwing a colourful rubber ball that squeaks on being squeezed, for me to catch—but I never bring it back to them.

My partner for my first studio session was Cousin Cosy, a Yorkshire terrier four years older than me and a girl.

At thirty-three months old, attempting a fitting mature look.

Chocolate's
Brown Study in the Bag

"Not all dogs stay quiet and motionless in a bag.
Only toy poodles can do it."

Rupert Chan

RUPERT CHAN is a university administrator, award winning playwright and lyricist, and a well-known versatile translator, writer, radio host, and opera commentator. Many are in his debt for his English sur-titles and sub-titles for Cantonese operas and films. He is Chairman of Directors of the Chung Ying Theatre Company and a Director of the Composers' and Authors' Society of Hong Kong (CASH). He has been an adviser on opera and drama to the Hong Kong Government's Leisure and Cultural Services Department. *Chocolate's Brown Study in the Bag* is Chan's second book in English. It won a place as a finalist in the inaugural (2009) Proverse Prize.

The Narrator of **CHOCOLATE'S BROWN STUDY IN THE BAG** is a thirty-three month old chocolate-coloured toy poodle, born in Australia and flown to Hong Kong for sale in a pet-shop. He has become a well-loved addition to a middle-class Hong Kong Chinese family who take him everywhere, sometimes (when the place is forbidden to dogs) hidden in a bag. Paradoxically, when zipped up in the pitch black darkness inside the bag and naturally entering into a brown study, he enters the colourful world of dreams, reviewing in them his past and present life.

As Chocolate tells his tale, we learn his human family's looks, habits, history, hobbies, education, professions, relationships, aspirations and thoughts. We meet his doggie friends and learn about the special world that dog-owners in Hong Kong inhabit. Unexpectedly, we also partake of the small dog's wisdom and learn the secret of happiness.

Chocolate's Brown Study in the Bag

Finalist for the Proverse Prize (2009)

Rupert Chan

Proverse Hong Kong

Chocolate's Brown Study in the Bag
by Rupert Kwan Yun Chan,   9 March 2011.
Copyright © Proverse Hong Kong, 9 March 2011.
1st published in Hong Kong by Proverse Hong Kong, 9 March 2011.
ISBN: 978-988-19932-1-2

Distribution (Hong Kong and worldwide): The Chinese University Press of
Hong Kong, The Chinese University of Hong Kong, Shatin, New Territories,
Hong Kong, SAR.
E-mail: cup@cuhk.edu.hk Tel: [INT+852] 2609-6508; Fax: [INT+852]
2603-7355
Web: http://www.chineseupress.com
Distribution (United Kingdom and worldwide except Hong Kong): Enquiries
and orders to Christine Penney, 28 West Street, Stratford-upon-Avon,
Warwickshire CV37 6DN, England.
Email: <clodpoll2001@yahoo.com>
Additional distribution: Proverse Hong Kong, P.O. Box 259, Tung Chung Post
Office, Tung Chung, Lantau, NT, Hong Kong, SAR.
Web: http://www.proversepublishing.com

The right of Rupert Kwan Yun Chan to be identified as the author of *Chocolate's Brown Study in the Bag* has been asserted by him in accordance with the Copyright, Designs and Patents Act 1988.

Printed in Hong Kong by Artist Hong Kong Company, Unit D3, G/F, Phase 3, Kwun Tong Industrial Centre, 448-458 Kwun Tong Road, Kowloon, Hong Kong.
Cover design by Proverse Hong Kong and Artist Hong Kong Company.
Page design, copy-editing and proof-reading by Proverse Hong Kong.

Proverse Hong Kong

British Library Cataloguing in Publication Data

Chan, Rupert.
  Chocolate's brown study in the bag.
  1. Toy poodle--China--Hong Kong--Fiction. 2. Dog
owners--China--Hong Kong--Fiction. 3. Autobiographical
fiction.
  I. Title II. Bickley, Gillian - III. Bickley, Verner
  Courtenay.
  823.9'2-dc22

  ISBN-13: 9789881993212

Table of Contents

Acknowledgements

We acknowledge with gratitude publication sponsorship from the Society for Abandoned Animals Limited.

Table of Illustrations

Aba in a Burberry shirt to catch up with my change of costume.	IX
Turned tails.	X
Phoebus, in polo shirt and jeans, borrowed a dog's bow tie and wore it to match my formal dress.	XI
Studio Paradiso (which sadly has now ceased operation).	XII
There was a snow-capped mountain against which I rode in a colourful toy convertible buggy.	XIII
Aba willingly serves as my prop for obstacle race practice.	XIV
"The way Chocolate runs, fore and hind legs alternately off the ground, ears and tail thrown up in the air—that's a beautiful picture of pure happiness!"	XIV
Ha ha ha! I am having a ball—I mean happy with my ball.	XV
They play fetch with me, throwing a colourful rubber ball that squeaks on being squeezed, for me to catch—but I never bring it back to them.	XV
My partner for my first studio session was Cousin Cosy, a Yorkshire terrier four years older than me and a girl.	XVI
At thirty-three months old, attempting a fittingly mature look.	XVI

Chocolate Introduces Himself

I am often zipped up in a bag by my parents and smuggled into all sorts of places I am not supposed to visit. Thus kept in the pitch-black darkness and keeping mum – a veritable brown study – paradoxically I start reminiscing about my bygone days, all thirty-three months of them, in a multi-coloured dreamland like Dorothy venturing from monochrome Kansas into Oz in the movie! My whole life, as people say, flashes across my mind's eyes in flashbacks of mingled reality and fantasy: my joys, my woes, my highs, my lows; my daily routines, my weekly fun times, my favourite flings, my direst dreads! And to crown it all, my family's unremitting love for me, in return for my devotion to them!

I am too small, and too puerile and naïve, to do any serious soul-searching or reflections on the meaning of my existence. But in my brown study in the bag I chronicle my virtual autobiography: at least Part One thereof.

Oh, allow me to introduce myself. I am Chocolate, my parents' last born – *à la* "last born boy clutches heart, last born girl clutches all five vital organs," as the Chinese saying goes, a toy poodle. Woof!

Chocolate's Brown Study in the Bag

1.   Shanghai Memories

At first, there was only silence.
And stillness.
All wrapped up in total darkness.
Then, all of a sudden, there was light!
A bright sun was shining above.
A boundless green lawn, bestrewn with flowers of every colour of the rainbow, stretched all around me as far as my eyes could see.
Again suddenly, without warning, some projectile flew overhead. From behind me, towards the distant horizon ahead. Just before it shrank into a dot, I made out what it was … a multi-coloured rubber ball, swiftly disappearing into the green green grass yonder.…
And then, just at this juncture when I was beginning to marvel at the gaudy panorama in sight, it all vanished abruptly!
Snapping out of it, I am back in the present. I will stick with the present, and hence the present tense.
I open my eyes, realizing only now that they have been shut, and that all that foregoing vista has been a dream.
And I realize what has roused me from my dream.
I am being carefully deposited on the floor.
To be precise, it is the bag in which I am snuggling that is being deposited.
On the carpeted floor of a spacious hall.
Carefully.
By Mimi, who sees to it that the bag remains standing erect, leaning against the legs of her chair.
A chair at a dining table. This is obviously a dining hall, an eating place, a restaurant.
Mimi is still fumbling nervously at the bag – I can feel her hands trembling – when a familiar voice warns her in a conspiratorial stage whisper:

11

"The waiter's coming!"

That voice belongs to Aba, and it's coming from across the table. I make out his legs sitting opposite Mimi. So they are having dinner here.

Panic-stricken at Aba's warning, Mimi hastily pushes the bag under her chair, with obvious furtiveness, and bestrides the chair corner with one trousered leg, apparently to hide the bag from sight.

"Good evening and welcome. Would you like to order some drinks first?" the waiter asks, making a half bow.

"Jasmine tea, and a pot of hot water too," replies Aba, with perfect aplomb.

"Very well, Sir." Leaving two menus with white covers bound in cellophane on the table, the waiter walks away.

All the while Mimi behaves like a kidnapper afraid of being caught red-handed.

In contrast, Aba and I exhibit great composure.

Well settled in the umbra beneath Mimi's chair, I peep through the meshes at the front end of the bag. A strange place, this. The stale smell of the food-stained carpet is unfamiliar: neither Italian nor Cantonese cuisine, as far as I can tell. I have definitely not been here before.

Not surprising, since I am just thirty-three months old.

Mimi darts another anxious look at the bag. Guilt is written all over her face.

Yes, just like a kidnapper afraid of exposure.

Afraid of letting the cat out of the bag?

But I am not a cat. I am Chocolate, Aba's and Mimi's last born.

"Aba," as distinct from "Abba," is pronounced "Aah Bah," in dropping intonation, as the British pronounce "arbour".

"Mimi" is not pronounced "Mimmy" as in *La Bohème*, but as if repeating "Me" in equally high pitch.

Aba and Mimi are variants of "Papa" and "Mammy" in

Cantonese. That is what this couple's children call them.

Starting with (or rather started by) Phoebe, their first born.

I have heard Aba explain how "Mimi" came about umpteen times, to various acquaintances. The young couple, as they were then, were living in a small two-room flat in Happy Valley, where the (then Royal) Hong Kong Jockey Club had (and still has) its headquarters. Phoebe was hardly one year old. In Aba's arms, at the foot of Shan Kwong Road, watching race horses march down from the stables at the hilltop to the race-course, Phoebe was taught to say "horse" in Cantonese – "Ma" – first, even before she learnt to address her Papa as "Aba". So when she was told to say "Mammy," she resisted. Absolutely refused to call her mother a horse. In the end, she reached a compromise with Aba her speech coach, viz. to repeat only the second syllable of Mammy, as a di-syllabic address – "Mimi". All her younger siblings (all boys) followed suit, showing respect for the eldest sister's form of address for their mother.

And I, Chocolate, am, in Mimi's own words, "her last born," *à la* "Last born boy clutches heart. Last born girl clutches all five vital organs," as the Chinese saying goes.

And I am a boy. Mimi says anybody can tell that from my perpetual silly boyish grin.

All that recollection of the origin of parental addresses takes only a second. About as long as that beautiful dream has taken – ah, so I do have coloured dreams! I must have dozed off, pent up in the dark inside the bag, when they were carrying me down the escalator to this basement storey restaurant.

Talk about their behaving like panic-stricken kidnappers afraid of being caught red-handed. And yet they have the audacity to have dinner at a Chinese restaurant!

Back to the black and white reality of the present.

"Still worried?" asks Aba, again with concern.

"Very much!" answers Mimi, "I can swear that waiter sensed I was hiding something under my chair."

"I'm not surprised if he did. Who wouldn't have? You behave like a kidnapper afraid of being caught. Or rather, asking to be caught."

"I AM afraid! Honest. Remember what happened at that Chinese restaurant – Chinese restaurants are so brightly lit – where the New China News Agency used to be?'

"Yes…"

"Chocolate was hidden in that black bag which was much more sealed up than this one. But that waitress had sharp eyes, could tell at once what was inside. And then she tipped off the maitre d', and he was all for shoving Chocolate, bag and baggage, in a closet while we dined! Only I insisted he stay by my side, and guaranteed he'd be no trouble at all."

"And that's just how he was!" Aba nonchalantly waves the incident away with his hand, "Well, we'll just never go there again and that's all there is to it. This place is different."

"How so?"

"This Shanghai Memories Restaurant used to be called Lao Zheng Xing Shanghai Restaurant, with a history of over sixty years. It used to be in Causeway Bay, just behind Mitsukoshi Department Store before that was pulled down."

"So?"

"We used to dine at that old location, and often ran into the Wills there. The Wills kept two giant huskies, remember? … when Barry was dean and they were living at staff quarters, two University Drive, on campus?"

"Things have changed," retorts Mimi, raising her voice. "The Wills moved out when Barry resigned, and your campus is now out of bounds to dogs."

I have a soft spot for Number Two University Drive. But

that's another story. Mimi lowers her voice and continues *sotto voce*, "I know. You're just trying to comfort me, by hinting that this is a canine-friendly place. I doubt it. But thanks for trying."

I deduce – for I cannot actually see it – that, in the ensuing noiseless pause, Mimi stretches out a hand to grasp Aba's. I know her well enough to guess what she is going to do at a moment like this.

But they are interrupted again.

"Hello, Mr and Mrs Chan. So good to see you again! And your sons are not joining you today? Quiet dinner for two, right?"

"Hello, Mr Zang!" Mimi returns the greeting to the intruder who is in black suit and tie. The name rings a bell: I've heard Mimi and Aba talk about him. Mr Zang was maître d' at the old place when it was known as Lao Zheng Xing, and is still *maître d'* here at Shanghai Memories. He knows the family and values them as loyal patrons.

Maître d'hôtel is of course a blown-up title, for he is only in the restaurant's employ, not the hotel's, though the restaurant does rent the basement of the hotel premises. In Hongkongese (a random mixture of English and Cantonese and the *lingua franca* used in everyday conversation in the multicultural metropolis of Hong Kong) the title is either the anglicized "Captain" (pronounced "cap duen" in Hong Kong style) or the sinicized "Bo Jeung" (buzhang in Putonghua, the same term as "Minister" – in the head of government ministry sense, not the clergyman sense – in Beijing or London).

Mr Zang is all smiles and bows, as he recommends seasonal dishes.

"Ready to order now? Try the bean sprouts, superbly fresh!...Your elder son is very talented! Saw him on TV so often... Or the drunken chicken. The chef's experimenting with our new shipment of rice wine from Shaoxing.... And how's your daughter overseas? Such a fine girl...."

Friendly chitchat soon warms the formerly tense atmosphere at the table to, "just like old times!"

Relaxed now, I settle into my favourite posture. Aba terms it "roast suckling pig," metaphorically referring to the standard starter at Cantonese banquets. I simply stretch out my fore legs fore and my hind legs aft in opposite directions as I lie flat on my stomach. The bottom padding of the bag, at once hard enough to give support and softened by stuffing for comfort, is snug and warm. Hence I am prone to doze off into my multi-coloured dreamland whenever I am shut up in the bag.

Being well-educated, or rather, well-trained, with a graduation certificate from an intermediate course at the obedience school of the (erstwhile Royal) Society for the Prevention of Cruelty to Animals (SPCA), I am extraordinarily well-disciplined and well-behaved. I will make no sound, and minimal movement, once I am placed inside the bag and it is zipped closed.

That has enabled me to remain in the company of Aba and Mimi virtually anywhere and everywhere.

For instance, they take me to mass on Sundays and Feast Days. I recall how once, when I was coming out of the bag outside the church after mass, an old lady in the same congregation saw me and remarked in amazement, "Christ! This is a puppy full of God's grace!"

Amen to that!

Of course, I am not always taken, hidden in the bag, only to such holy places as masses and churches. I have happy memories of being taken on bus rides, on underground rides (at the risk of a heavy fine if found out!), on ferry rides to outlying islands.... And of course, to numerous meals from fast food or dim sum lunches, to posh grills, to Chinese birthday banquets lasting hours!

They even took me to see a movie once!

It was Mid-Autumn Festival, 2007 and I had just turned one year old. The moon is at its roundest and brightest on this Mid-Autumn night in the lunar calendar. It being a public holiday, Lena was off. (Lena is the one in the household who has the same complexion as mine.) Hence Aba and Mimi had to take me along with them to lunch at Yung Kee Restaurant in the Central District – one among the top ten restaurants worldwide. After lunch, they carried me, in the bag, into Queen's Theatre in its last days before demolition, to watch Ang Lee's *Lust • Caution.*

At any other cinema, the big bag was sure to arouse suspicion – of containing a camcorder for piracy purposes – and get searched. But who'd care at a cinema soon to close down?

"When it came to .that scene when army dogs – Alsatians – appeared, searching for guerrillas and barking fiercely, my heart almost leapt out of my mouth! I was so scared Chocolate in the bag would respond!" Mimi is never tired of recounting this incident to her friends. No sweat... I slept through the whole show.

That is what I usually do when in the bag, half dozing off, half pensive, in a brown study.

We like this arrangement on Lena's off days: Aba and Mimi would rather have me by their side, though shut up in a bag. I would rather be so than left home alone.

Not all dogs stay quiet and motionless in a bag. Only toy poodles can do it.

2.   Seth

Only toy poodles can stay noiseless and motionless in a bag.

However, all dogs have short memories.

That is why dogs are always cheerful.

We leave all unhappy recollections behind, and selectively recall only the happy good old days.

Toy poodles have a high IQ.

We have the highest IQ among small dogs, second only to border collies, which are big dogs, who claim the highest IQ among all dogs.

We toy poodles can retain things we are taught much longer. That means we also retrieve unhappy memories, on a need basis, to learn from mistakes and painful experience.

I have no memory of my natural mother. Or of my Motherland for that matter.

Must have had my eyes shut most of the time during those first two months of my life, sucking my mother's milk, back in Australia, where I was born on 21 August 2006.

Nor do I remember the long flight to Hong Kong, immediately after weaning, again asleep most of the time, locked up in the cargo cabin.

Nor do I retain the equally unpleasant memory of being locked up, after landing, in that glass-paned show-window of a cage – one among many cages arrayed like pigeon holes – in the pet shop in Hong Kong.

But I remember every detail of the story of Seth, which Aba and Mimi keep retelling *ad nauseam*.

About the time when I was born "down under", Aba and Mimi had just returned to Hong Kong after a package tour to Australia, followed by a further week's stay at Phoebe's flat in Sydney. Phoebe, an LSE graduate in accountancy, had gone to work in the Land of Oz.

The couple found their second born boy Phoebus (a

music graduate at a local university) waiting for them at home, together with Seth, a three-year old red toy poodle. Phoebus had started his own production house, and Marsha – singer/dancer/model/movie star – then on location shooting abroad, had entrusted her pet Seth to the care of Phoebus, her Manager on the singing side.

Seth stayed only two weeks, but that was long enough to win the love, or at least infatuation, of Phoebus's parents. Toy poodles are descendants of circus performers and entertainer blood runs in the family. Probably because he followed Marsha's singing practice closely, Seth could sing accurately (with a "woof" syllable like a wolf's howling) the top note of an arpeggio played on the piano by Phoebus or sung by his girlfriend Danielle. Also probably because he had to accompany Marsha to such restricted areas as location shooting, backstage, changing rooms and movie studios, etcetera, he was trained to stay quiet in a zipped-up bag for hours on end. So he also accompanied his temporary minders to meals at restaurants without any problem.

But what captured Aba's and Mimi's hearts were not bags of tricks, but affection pure and simple.

The couple, still on summer vacation, took Seth on long walks up Hatton Road, in their neighbourhood, all the way to Victoria Peak. Seth obviously enjoyed very much what must have been a rare pastime for him. He walked on his own, without a leash, but always keeping Mimi and Aba in sight. He was noticeably gratified that they were taking him on outings for exercise he badly needed. On one such hike, Mimi went into the public lavatory at the Peak, bidding Aba to take Seth and walk on ahead, and she would catch up with them. To her surprise, when she came out she found Seth sitting by the road waiting. The cleaner who minded the public lavatory told her, "He wouldn't go. He wanted to wait for Mama!" That was how he captured Mimi's heart.

So it was not surprising that, when the fortnight was up and Seth was reclaimed by Marsha, Mimi was heartbroken. She began to weep in bed at night, languishing like a teenage girl separated from her first love.

Well, Aba often boasted about how he won Mimi's love as her first suitor in her teenage years: she kept a collie and a mongrel at that time, also living in Happy Valley. He was ever ready to accompany her walking her dogs. And when the collie had skin trouble and was shaven bald, so ugly that none of Mimi's family would brave the disgrace of walking him, Aba remained true and walked the collie regularly, thus winning the devotion of both dog and owner.

And now, thirty years after those first pets had passed away – the mongrel lived to the ripe old age of twenty-one, in time to see Phoebe learning to walk, chasing him and pushing his tail for fun, when he was too senile to mind the disrespect of this infantile prank – Mimi experienced sentimental attachment to a canine again.

Aba himself was swept off his feet by Seth as well. In September 2006, Phoebus organized a lunchtime charity concert for the University of Hong Kong (HKU) at the Sun Yat-Sen Plaza on campus. Marsha was one of the performers. Her mother Pei Pei, a veteran movie star, in Hong Kong and elsewhere – she was the villain nanny who killed the hero (played by Chow Yun Fat) with a poison dart in Ang Lee's award-winning movie, *Crouching Tiger and Hidden Dragon* – was sitting in the audience, a zipped up bag on her lap. Aba, who worked at the University, passed by after lunch, spotted her and sat down beside her to say hello. Without warning, the bag on her lap suddenly leapt to life, the zip was forced open, and Seth's head emerged, giving a yelp of joy and recognition, before licking Aba all over the face incessantly, in great excitement! All that remaining quiet and still in a zipped up bag training was thrown to Timbuctoo! All because he sensed his beloved pet-sitter was nearby.

Since then, Aba had joined Mimi in her nightly languishing!

That was when the three children realized that they had a crisis on their hands. Phoebe was working abroad. Fabian the youngest – his name betrayed the plain fact that it was an unexpected afterthought: after his parents had run out of "Moon Sister, Sun Brother" Grecian names – was still studying in North America. Phoebus was the only one in Hong Kong, so busy at his business and keeping such late hours that his parents hardly ever saw him even though they all lived under the same roof.

The children held an emergency teleconference on how to handle the lovelorn parents, and reached consensus on the only feasible solution. Aba and Mimi would be celebrating their thirtieth wedding anniversary in December 2006. Their offspring jointly offered to buy them a Pearl Wedding present: a new pet to keep them company – in place of the grown-up trio scattered asunder – as the parents' last born. (And let him clutch their hearts!)

And so it came to pass that Mimi dried her tears and shopped around in exhilaration instead. She left orders at pet shops all around town for a toy poodle – of dark chocolate colour, so as to be distinct from the popular red colour, the colour of Seth. And Aba surfed pet shop websites looking for dark chocolate colour pooches.

Aba and Mimi were soon called up and invited to drop into a pet shop in Causeway Bay, to inspect a dark chocolate toy poodle newly brought out to the city from the breeding farm in the New Territories. Like all locally bred toy poodles, this one had its tail cut short at birth and styled into a ball, as was Seth's. Also, the price asked was exorbitant. Aba and Mimi were hesitant.

Then came the day I landed in Hong Kong, in late October 2006. The pet shop I was caged in called Mimi at once to announce my arrival. Aba and Mimi came over that very evening. It was love at first sight. I was taken home on Sunday, 29 October 2006, and became Mimi's last born.

Thank you, Seth, you have served as my prologue! Seth set the scene for me to make my entrance.

Therefore I choose to remember him in a positive light.

I only met him once, during the Christmas season at the end of 2006. Marsha and her Mom went on a family reunion trip to the West Coast of USA and Seth was left in Mimi's care for a second time. The difference this time was that I was there, living in my play-pen placed in a corner of the living room. I remember Seth as a fellow toy poodle and playmate for a short while. I deliberately erase all other memories.

Such as that day when Rufina, Mimi's goddaughter, called at our house. Mimi reproached me for what the evidence pointed to, my wetting the floor within the bounds of my play-pen. "You forgot your house-training? Chocolate, you naughty boy!"

And it was Rufina who exonerated me from blame. "But I saw it was Seth lifting his hind leg and pissing into Chocolate's play-pen!"

Then the two women discussed whether it was jealousy leading to wilful framing of Chocolate – which would suggest very high, though crooked, intelligence in Seth – or pure territorial instinct.

Me? I couldn't care less which it was. I will always remember Seth as my very good friend.

"Like Proteus to Valentine," observed Aba, from his experience in translating/adapting *The Two Gentlemen of Verona* to an early Republic of China setting. (In his Chinese version, the Two Gentlemen were rivals on the staff of a warlord (the Duke in the original) in the martial arts city of Foshan in Guangdong Province.)

To complete the story of Seth, he was originally a present from Marsha's ex-boyfriend, kept by Marsha long after they broke up. When Marsha worked in Shanghai for a protracted period, Seth was a temporary immigrant there, to keep her company. But in the end, Seth became a permanent resident of Los Angeles, after Marsha visited her elder sister there and decided that Seth would be happier there with all the open air life that it offered. And so Seth stayed on in L.A. I never saw him again. If you ask me, the open air in L.A. is not that superior to that in Hong Kong. I've heard Aba talk about the smog there and how people there wake up to the sound of birds coughing!

The last I know, Marsha's ex-boyfriend, a TV star and singer, was reported to have wept in public, in front of fans and reporters, when he learned of the migration of Seth.

"Knowing Seth and what he must mean to his one-time owner, I believe his tears were true!" observed Mimi on reading the news report.

"We miss Seth too," meditated Aba, "come to think of it, if they were willing to part with Seth after all, they might have agreed to let us keep Seth if we'd asked."

"It's karma," responded Mimi, "that it's Chocolate that we get to keep, not Seth."

3.   Early Childhood

My reminiscence of Seth is cut short when I am recalled to the present by Mr Zang's "That should do for two!" in *sforzando*, after his protracted recommendation of dishes in a subdued murmur.

As he walks away, I believe I hear what sounds like "Phew", in unison from my parents.

Sorry, Mimi and Aba, for causing you worry and angst. You are always so unfailingly protective of me. I just cannot understand what you see in me.

In fact, I wonder what you saw in me on that aforementioned occasion of love at first sight.

I can understand the vogue for pets in a hectic urban community like Hong Kong, where human beings are disillusioned and even despairing of members of their own species. I can understand the popularity of toy poodles too, given our inherent talents, reinforced by the Japanese fad of giving toy poodles that cute teddy bear look. Hong Kong-bred toy poodles all adopt that same coiffure, and have their tails docked at birth into balls.

I was distinct from all other toy poodles in that pet shop, which was my first stop in Hong Kong, not just in the colour of my fur – dark chocolate as opposed to the popular red (actually a lighter brown) and apricot (a colour which they term "tea with milk" in Hong Kong) – but in my bushy long tail as well. Docking tails is not allowed in Australia.

As an Ozzie baby my hairdo was also markedly different from the teddy bear look of my cage-mates. I had my muzzle close-cropped, in the traditional hairstyle of poodles in Europe and North America.

"He's like a fox." That was Aba's first impression.

"Or a mouse," commented Mimi in turn.

I was therefore quite certain that they would choose my cage-mate in red, whom Mimi fondly called "Sweet Potato".

25

He was cuter, plumper and much more energetic, back at the pet shop, than the skinny, lethargic yours truly still suffering from jet lag.

And I was very dark then, like dark chocolate, hence my subsequent christening as Chocolate, by Mimi.

Not any more.

Now I conform to fashion and exhibit a teddy bear coiffure, with legs like flared trousers having longer hair, close-cropped body with a slim waistline, and a muzzle all fluffy.

"Like a chocolate muffin!" as Mimi describes it.

But I still flaunt a long bushy tail.

And my fur gets lighter and lighter in colour, as I grow up. Now I am more like milk-chocolate.

"Or mouldy chocolate," suggests Aba, with sarcasm.

No, not photogenic at all, am I!

Mimi has made many unsuccessful attempts at taking pictures of me since my infancy. But my eye-balls and nose (and paws too, for that matter) were all the same dark brown colour. As a result, looking at my pictures, nobody could make out my features. And if Mimi used flash, my eye pupils would show a macabre, satanic red glow!

My reflections in the bag thereupon jump to Aba, who keeps a whole lot of my photos, all laminated for durability, in his wallet. He never hesitates to show them to fellow dog-owners anywhere, with paternal pride!

The earliest one shows me newly arrived home at two months old, with my above-mentioned foxy/mousy face, chewing on Mimi's leather slipper on the carpet. A peanut-shaped cotton toy, my very first chew-toy bought at the pet shop on the day I was taken home from there, was lying beside me. This picture is the historical record of my size then: the same size as the slipper or the peanut. Now the peanut is just the length of my hind leg (which is just right! More of it later).

However, Mimi and Aba keep very few pictures of me sleeping in my pen. On my part, I also deliberately retain minimal memories of those infant play-pen days, as is my habit with any unpleasant experience.

Not only was I virtually incarcerated within the confines of the pen, it also meant I was sleeping alone at night, an unbearable torment for a toy poodle! It was little comfort (mentally and sentimentally) that I was provided with my own cosy little round crib placed inside the pen. Still less the fact that Aba sang lullabies to put me to sleep every night…

"Just as I sang lullabies for Phoebe, Phoebus and Fabian in their infancy," reminisced Aba, with warmth and self-satisfaction.

"Yeah, and that's why we never had enough sleep as babies!" chimed his children in unisonantly chilly riposte.

Same here! How I wished he wouldn't! Sing, that is, when I was trying to get some repose!

While on the subject, with their rewarding experience of training Seth to sing the top notes of arpeggios, Phoebus and Fabian attempted to start my music training at as early a stage of life as their own.

They would play little ditties on the grand piano in the far corner of the dining-room, coaxing and encouraging me to sing along. Fabian would play either a Beethoven sonata (usually Opus 13, the *Pathétique*) or one of the pieces played by Jay Chou (the Taiwan pop singer/movie star) in his piano duel movie. Phoebus had a wider repertoire. (Nancy Loo, Phoebe's piano teacher in Hong Kong, once observed sarcastically that Phoebus had the rare talent of playing Chopin with an Eason Chan flavour, and vice versa, whatever that means. – Eason Chan is a Hong Kong pop singer/movie star, in case you don't know.) But they both soon found that I lacked the kind of perfect pitch gift that Seth had shown.

And yet they were not disappointed, nor loved me less for my deficiency, nor did I display any inferiority complex. Keeping up with the Joneses is simply not in my nature. I was a good sport and sang in my "woof, woof" syllables to their playing. I did have a hard time, though, keeping up when Phoebus played *Flight of the Bumble Bee*, or Chopin's *Revolutionary Etude*, the one common number which all three of them, Phoebe, Phoebus and Fabian, could play.

However bad my singing, I honestly have always tried my best. It was appreciated and invariably I received a pat on the head with the verbal accolade, "Good boy." Phoebus once put on his website a video recording of my singing along to his rendering of *Flight of the Bumble Bee*. The family enjoyed watching it, and has kept on upbraiding Phoebus ever since he deleted it.

Singing and getting commended for it is one thing worth remembering from my infant days.

That was also my house-training period. Of course I am averse to recall having the "pan" next to my crib in the pen! The "pan" was just the shape and size of the tray you use at McDonald's, but lined with water absorbent padding. Now that I only wee wee and poo poo outdoors, I try my best to forget those sleeping-next-to-my-indoor-loo days.

In any case my play-pen days were not that long. By Christmas I could climb the fence-like side. My New Year resolution in 2007 was to scale new heights. And I soon did. I discovered I could actually jump over the side and be free of the confinement of the pen! By Chinese New Year, the pen had served its historical mission, was dismantled and put away, and I have ever since been sleeping in Aba's and Mimi's king-size bed in the master bedroom.

I have a habit of showing my ecstasy at my favourite spots: by lying supine and rolling this way and that with glee. I do that every night after jumping into bed, rolling on the bedcover. My exposed belly in the supine posture is at once a sign of my total trust in my parents beside me, as well as being inviting to them. They can never resist my seductive disposition and will always stroke my stomach fondly. I am happy to say that, ever since our becoming bed-fellows, Aba has ceased to sing lullabies, replacing that with this intimate caress as a prelude to our synchronized retirement, much to my relief.

I also adopt that posture – of lying supine and rolling about – at other favourite spots: on the turf in the Pinewood Battery picnic area half way up Hatton Road, on the Mount Austin turf up at the Peak, and on the lawn of the Wanchai Waterfront Promenade – "Dogs' Park" to Mimi – although she insists we have our romp on the planked seafront part of the Park, for good reasons. … In fact, we've just been there before coming to this restaurant, two blocks inshore from Dogs' Park.

"Plop!"

A thick piece of cloth suddenly falls – from Mimi's lap apparently – and lands just beside the bag, rousing me from my reminiscence.

Mimi stoops to pick it up, and takes the opportunity – I am not sure if she drops the napkin on purpose – to give me an affectionate peep through the meshes. Our eyes meet. I can clearly see the love and care in her stare. She clearly cannot see my eyes, but seems to sense I am staring back with equal warmth and attachment!

I expect this exchange of loving looks to be followed by a fitting gesture, either stroking my belly or a pat on my head.

I get something in between: she pats the bag fondly. I crane my neck to receive this anticipated token of love, notwithstanding the barrier of the zipped bag top, with my head. Thanks, Mimi! I will always cherish your tender loving care.

Exercising my selective recollection, I make an effort to

block out the awful memories of my operation at six months old, even though it was no less a manifestation of Mimi's Tender Loving Care for me.

She took the vet's advice to have me neutered at the earliest opportunity, so I wouldn't have prostate cancer and would live longer. I was put under General Anaesthetic and, as I later gathered, in the middle of the operation, the vet rang up Mimi to recommend and obtain her consent to use the opportunity to fix my hernia and also extract my milk teeth which were growing sideways. So he killed three birds while I was once stoned!

Naturally I am loath to remember the stitches on my tummy, or those long miserable days of wearing the "lamp shade" around my head to prevent my licking my wound.

"Is that a satellite TV receptor? Ho, ho, ho!" All my neighbours laughed at me. Esteban the miniature bull terrier, whom I frequently tease by pouncing on his back, did it in retaliation. Emily the golden retriever, did it in typical feminine ghoulishness.

Only Cardos the Labrador upstairs was a true gentleman. He remained kindly to me, slapping me this way and that by wagging his huge tail in the cramped elevator when we were riding in it together.

That was the gloomiest week of my early childhood.

4. Daily Routine

No, I am not too keen to recall my early childhood days of imprisonment in the pen.

I'd rather remember my happy daily routine since coming out of the pen.

Weekends are great. Weekdays are not bad either.

I stir slightly in the bag, stimulated by the scent invading my nostrils. I can tell precisely what is happening at the table above my head. Even though I cannot see it, I can visualize everything to the last detail by using my nose. Aba is sipping his cup of jasmine tea and Mimi, her cup of water – she never takes tea after sundown – each washing down roasted peanuts from the snack bowl. One peanut drops on the table, rolls to the table-edge and falls down on the carpeted floor right next to my bag. (The bag is habitable for hours because the meshes allow me to breathe and see the outside world clearly as if through a one-way mirror. I, on the other hand, cannot be seen from the outside, being dark myself and also sitting in the dark.) That roasted peanut smells so good and strongly that, even though it is out of reach, I cannot help stirring again.

Just as I do every morning in bed, when the alarm clock goes off at daybreak (and before daybreak in winter, when it is still dark), I stir, disturbing Aba sleeping next to me, and starting a chain reaction. He stretches out a sleepy hand to locate me, often finding Mimi's hand reaching out for the same purpose. And then, action! Aba the earliest riser starts his day (still sleepily) with stroking my tummy, then goes out for his morning walk, to practise Qigong. Next, Mimi gets up, puts on her make up and gets dressed – after washing herself of course – all done busily and hurriedly in an amazingly short space of time, and goes off to work a smashing beauty. She looks like, and indeed is, a model.

Or rather, a role-model, for looking your best every

morning, for her classes of primary school-girls. She is a teacher and, since qualifying for the teaching profession decades ago, has been teaching in the same school as where she completed her own primary and secondary education. She has therefore spent the greater part of her life at one and the same institution, except for the couple of years when she was training as a teacher at a college of education. And consequently she has watched some of her very first students grow up, graduate and later return to the school as her new colleagues. But she manages to look and feel just as young as they.

Often asked by her friends how she can stick to one job and one school for life without getting fed up, Mimi explained, "Never a dull moment! Primary schoolgirls are so unpredictable and spontaneous. And each year you see a new batch of primary one admissions. They show their genuine devotion and adoration for me their teacher by racing to be the first to arrive at school each morning and the first to hug me by my legs, like hugging a tree! And I give them pictures of Chocolate as rewards for doing well in class."

I had a good laugh, as did Aba, when Mimi told him how, on one of the days when she was particularly gorgeously attired, a primary-one student in her class observed, "You're dressed like a 'company person' today". By 'company person' the little girl meant an OL (as Office Ladies are called in Hong Kong).

Every weekday morning, at 7.30 sharp, Lena takes me downstairs to see Mimi off, for her to give me kisses and pats before driving off to school. Then, before I take my own morning walk to poo poo and wee wee, I will first inspect my Guard of Honour, escorted by Lena as my aide-de-camp. The Guard of Honour is made up of school children in the neighbourhood, all dressed up snazzily in school uniform.They stand lining the sidewalk just outside our building, waiting for their school bus. Their mothers or domestic helpers accompany them, holding their school bags and water bottles for them. I routinely stride past them assuming the air of a general inspecting his troops. My poodle gait is by nature an elegant trot, like a horse performing in dressage. That adds to my majesty. And they all hail me warmly, my Guard of Honour do! Why, I even occasionally do them the extra honour of inspecting the interior of their school bus as well when it arrives and pulls over. The bus driver will salute me smartly, and respectfully waits until I complete my inspection and alight, before he dares to drive off.

Aba remarked, in mid 2007, "I've lived here in this building for eight years. Hardly any neighbours know me. Chocolate's been here eight months. And the whole neighbourhood know and greet him, from street cleaners to expatriate housewives."

Sour grapes!

The fragrance entering my nostrils changes. The waiter has just brought the first cold dishes: drunken chicken with the strong rice wine flavour and shredded jellyfish. (I can never understand why humans would eat such cold flaccid dead animals!)

Mimi and Aba raise their chopsticks, and I continue my reverie about my daily schedule, by coincidence just coming to breakfast time.

I am back from my morning walk and Lena gives me breakfast and water in my set of twin dishes on the tiled kitchen floor. It takes me just a jiffy to finish both dishes. Now the other family members get up and breakfast one by one before they go to work. Fabian leaves home first. Then Aba, back from his morning exercise, takes his healthy meal dictated by Mimi. It comprises "five-green" juice (a blend of green apples, celery, cucumber, bitter gourd and green pepper – a repulsive green slime!), sliced papaya, a bowl of vegetables, and another bowl of either oatmeal or rice congee. Anyone starting the day with such revolting ingestion deserves my heartfelt sympathy! Finally, sometime before noon, Phoebus has brunch prepared by Lena, or sometimes nothing at all if he is in a hurry.

Well, inevitably I digress to ponder with self-confidence that puppies have a keen sense of domestic hierarchy, and accord a commensurate and appropriate degree of respect to each household member. Mimi is the undisputed supreme monarch and commander-in-chief in our household. Next comes Aba, his ranking being primarily by virtue of seniority, but also as a compassionate concession that acknowledges his obedience in allowing Mimi to run him. Then there is Lena who stays at home all day to look after my meals and "convenience walks", and keep me company. Her rank is ascribed by merit.

The worst times of the week are her shopping day afternoons, when she goes to the markets, including super- (i.e. dry) and wet, leaving me home alone for an hour. She turns on the television set for my sake but it is no help. Colour TV means nothing to my monochrome eyesight. And the images, even in HD, are to me nothing but two-dimensional pictures on a flat screen. I seldom react to TV shows, except when the family watches *101 Dalmatians*. Then I am attracted by the large number of puppies and their yapping.

For me, being left home alone in an empty house is indisputably the most intolerable torture. Far worse than hunger. I MUST have some family member's company. That's why, flash forwarding to dusk onwards, when each family member returns home after work, I welcome each and every one as he or she comes in with genuine gusto! The usual sequence is Lena after shopping, then Aba and Mimi "at twilight time" as the Platters chanted in their hit, and then Fabian, late at night.

And so back to the hierarchy. Phoebus comes home latest – or is it earliest? – in the small hours. However, he will always hear me wake up barking in the master bedroom, sensing his return, fetch me out and frolic with me heartily before sending me back in to continue my slumber. He kicks up a rumpus with me again when he gets up in the late morning, often spending the time on play at the expense of brunch, before going to work. That's why I fancy him, my heartiest playmate – my life-size toy as he calls himself – even though he is low on the totem pole of hierarchy, spending so little time at home.

As for Fabian, in my view his status is below mine. I landed from down under and came into the household first, in October 2006. He appeared only the following summer, home from North America. – I don't care whether he was born or brainwashed there; in either case he joined the family later than I. Hence his inferior position.

My view was confirmed when I heard Mimi say as much to Aba. "Come to think of it, there is truth in the saying 'Last born boy clutches heart'. You know how we decided not to take leave and fly over to attend Phoebe's graduation at LSE and my elder brother in London showed up on our behalf, calling me heartless. We also gave Fabian's graduation – held in winter snow at UMich – the miss."

"Yes, and even Phoebus's congregation locally. I attended alone, without you," added Aba.

"It's just too much trouble for me to take leave in my profession. And yet we went to Chocolate's graduation at obedience school together!"

Of course, it was as much a course for training them as for me, and we all got full marks for attendance, classes being held at weekends!

I can't help jumping back and forth and digressing. My mind reflects my nature. I jump around a lot too, physically.

To continue my diary, actually I spend most of my

weekday afternoons catching up on lost sleep. As I have said – I mean reminisced – I wake up several times a night. Aba is the one who goes to bed earliest, and I jump into bed with him. Mimi joins us later. But she reads in bed up to very late. Meanwhile, Fabian comes in after his long day at an investment bank. He never talks about his work at home, as he declares he shouldn't, couldn't and won't. Only after the Lehmann Brothers collapse did he once break his rule and lament in front of us all that, after he has worked in it for only a year, his chosen career has, alas, already become a sunset industry!

The point I am making is, I have usually fallen asleep in bed, together with Aba, by the time Fabian comes in. But once he does, I wake up instinctively, start barking with joy, dash out of the bedroom – Mimi from within, or Fabian from without, will open the bedroom door for me – and give him his well earned welcome. Too bad Fabian was born too late to know the Beatles' "A Hard Day's Night", which is an apt depiction of the situation.

Then he has his late supper, reheated by Lena, who has stirred from her room. And I go back to sleep – until hours later when Phoebus comes in, when I repeat the ritual (this time sans Lena and *sans souper*).

That's why I need that siesta to catch up on lost repose.

I've said I fancy Phoebus, for being wildly frolicsome any time he sees me, whatever the hour. He either chases me round and round the coffee table, or catches me and hoists me high up in his arms, or tosses me up in the air and catches me. (Aba also makes an attempt to humour me and chase me round the coffee table when he returns from his morning exercise, but he does it only feebly, and it's no fun at all.)

The latest mystery was an apparent crack – on investigation, fortunately found to be only a short, slight scratch – on the glass, protecting the gigantic Chinese painting of the Three Gorges, hanging on the living room wall. – The frame actually cost more, being made to order in Hong Kong, than the painting itself, bought in Hangzhou from a poverty-stricken street painter. – Phoebus was found guilty without trial since he was prone to throw tennis balls around, to play with me; and considered therefore the most likely culprit!

No wonder I can't help maintaining a liking for Phoebus, my indefatigable playmate. So in the morning, after everyone else has gone to work, I sometimes condescend to enter Phoebus's room and nestle in his bed until he gets up.

And when he does, he trains his sleepy eyes on me with such an expressive look, that I can hear him mentally singing the first verse of "My Cup Runneth Over With Love".

He is the black sheep in the family – even though it is I who am darker in complexion. All three of them in the second generation – to make up for what Aba missed in his own childhood – started music lessons at a very early age. But while Phoebe and Fabian had the same destiny of winning the overall championship in their very first piano competition, Phoebus lost in his. So the parents concentrated their efforts and expectations on the two winners, and Phoebus was left to struggle on his own.

Phoebe obtained the Licenciate of the Royal Schools of Music (Performing) at the age of thirteen, won a full scholarship and went to study at Wells Cathedral, a music school, in Somerset, England. (Mimi felt a pang of grief and wept when she visited Phoebe there for the first time one dreary winter, discovering that it went dark at 3pm, and the dormitory in the old castle had barred windows – "Just like a dungeon!")

Fabian had a will of his own from early childhood. When in primary school, he came home one night and told his parents, "The teacher asked me to be pianist for the school choir. I turned her down." He never thought of seeking his parents' consent first.

Then, after GCSE in the Fifth Form, Phoebe rebelled. She was fed up with her life being predominated by piano-playing and piano-practice, at the cost of no basketball lest she hurt her fingers, no time for other sports such as swimming in which she excelled, even no swotting for tests and examinations until after practising the piano. She gave up the scholarship and her music studies, transferred to St Paul's Girls' School in London for her Sixth Form studies and read accountancy at the London School of Economics, instead of pursuing a career in music. (All the same, she did continue to have private piano lessons at the Royal Academy of Music with Christopher Elton as her tutor.)

"I'd rather be an accountant who plays the piano as a hobby," said she.

In his turn, Fabian declared after completing Fourth Form that he wanted to swot for the School Certificate Examination (the Hong Kong equivalent of GCSE) and give up piano lessons in Fifth Form. He made his parents send him to Sevenoaks, Kent for Sixth Form studies, on the grounds that "everyone in our clan has studied overseas!" (Phoebus did Secondary School Grades 11 and 12 in Canada, and spent a freshman year reading biochemistry at Queen's University, Kingston, before coming back to a university in Hong Kong as an exchange student, in the event staying on to complete a degree in music.)

At Sevenoaks, Fabian wrote back to say he had resumed taking piano lessons because "You don't get dates if you don't play the piano". He then went on to do industrial engineering and economics at the University of Michigan (UMich), Ann Arbor, and finished up in an I-Bank.

So it has turned out that Phoebus was the only child who kept up his interest in music and made it his career choice.

During his undergraduate days, he started playing the piano in Times Square shopping mall, Causeway Bay. He first played there, in fact, in his secondary school days, as accompanist to a pop singer's show, and later served as rehearsal pianist for a local production of *Aida,* all as summer jobs.

After his graduation, when he became a weekend fixture playing the piano at Harbour City across Hong Kong harbour – he was the very first to be given the title "Prince of the Piano" by his fans – Phoebus had the unhappy experience of overhearing a mother in the audience telling her kid, "Son, see that big boy playing the piano? Learn a lesson from him. You must work hard at school, or else you'll end up having to do something like that for a living!"

That gave him the motivation to make mall-playing a Hong Kong subculture, and he succeeded.

He realized that playing classical music in a mall is at best a background music performance. No interaction. No interest aroused. So he started taking requests from mall shoppers attracted by his playing, who stopped to listen and watch. He would ask them to hum the melody of the request – most often a pop tune that he didn't know – and then played the tune by ear. That feat was what gained him so many fans.

He has one achievement in common with Aba. A considerable number of local university students in Hong Kong have done studies and written theses about Aba's sinicized translations/adaptations of Western drama. Particularly notable are Aba's transposition of *Twelfth Night* and *Cyrano de Bergerac* to Tang Dynasty China, where poets wear swords and speak Tang poems in place of the original lines. Others Aba has transposed to 1930s Hong Kong: *Pygmalion, Hobson's Choice, Volpone* and George Feydeau's *L'Hotel du Libre Echange.* A comparably not insignificant number have done similar studies on Phoebus as pioneer of music performances in shopping malls.

Many followed Phoebus's example, started as mall performers, and became pop singers. He himself insisted he preferred backstage to front stage work. This was even after accompanying celebrated virtuosi such as violinists, David Garrett and Huang Meng-la – each played the same piece, Monti's *Czardas*, in different styles and tempi, at the same mall and the same function – and singers, Huang Ying and Connie Talbot.

And I discover Phoebus and I share one common talent: our ears are quicker and sharper than our eyes!

Where was I?

Oh yes, the daily routine on weekdays....

Lena is very attached to me. She tells Mimi that she's much happier after I joined the household that she'd worked in for two decades (since Fabian was only two). Unlike Fabian who was scared of Lena the first time he saw her – when she came into his nursery all black with only two shining eyes and two rows of white teeth visible – I felt an instant affinity with Lena who has my same colour of skin – or, rather, fur in my case.

She is very considerate. When building maintenance work was going on in the flat below, making a lot of noise, she was worried that when she left me home alone I might be very frightened with all that hullabaloo. So she changed her schedule and went shopping in the late morning when I was safe in Phoebus's bed.

And in the evening, after dinner, Mimi and Aba – or sometimes Aba alone if Mimi has to work on setting or marking papers, or needs to watch soap opera on TV "so she can participate in the conversation of her workmates" – take me walking as a routine nocturnal pastime.

That is when I meet all my neighbouring friends, Cardos, Esteban, Emily, the whole gang. (We keep different hours for our daytime walks, and when they pass by my building then, each starts barking, its walker calls "Chocolate!" and I go out on the balcony to look down through the railings and greet them in return.)

Their Chinese owners always clean up after them (though in fact they seldom walk their dogs), and so do their more usual walkers who are Lena's compatriots...always that is except when they are preoccupied with talking on their mobile phones, when they neglect to clean up. The worst offenders are Caucasians. They walk or jog in a carefree manner, with their dogs unleashed and running ahead or after them, and clearly have no intention of bothering to clean up, not even bringing the necessary equipment for the purpose.

And when it rains, Aba and Mimi take me in the car to Two University Drive on the campus nearby to wee wee and poo poo at the covered undercroft there. This has become my sheltered private privy.

After the evening walk and back in the lift lobby of our building, I am unleashed and allowed to play "fetch" with a squeaky rubber ball for a while before going home. This greatly delights the night-watchman, who watches this free entertainment to break the monotony. Occasionally Rumble the bull-dog happily joins me in the game. Poor Rumble is much neglected by his owners, but his domestic helper loves him, even buying him toys out of her own pocket.

Back at home, Mimi's nightly ritual of brushing my fur and my teeth preludes bedtime.

"Toy poodles have naturally curly fur and it must be brushed twice daily at least, to keep it tidy. Oral hygiene is most important for his quality of life, to keep his teeth healthy right into old age. If one loves ones pet, these tasks will not be a daily chore, but rather something one enjoys as a pastime!" expounds Mimi to many a whining fellow pet owner.

That completes the daily routine on weekdays.

5. Vincent and Maggie

I live for the present. And I live for the weekends!

Like just now at Dogs' Park! Let me reminisce about this beautiful Sunday afternoon there…

But once again I – I mean we – are interrupted.

A chubby chap comes from two tables away, and pats Aba on the back heartily.

"Fancy running into you again! We do have the same taste, don't we?"

"Hello, Vincent," Aba greets this new intruder with visible delight.

"Last time, where did I run into you? – Yung Kee, that's it, just before you were going to take your Chocolate to watch *Love · Caution*," Vincent goes on to ask, "And is he here too?"

"Yes, that unforgettable adventure," muse Aba and I together, and then he proceeds to answer that last question, "And yes, he's here," throwing, as he speaks, a sidelong glance in my bag's direction. The two friends exchange a knowing nod.

"Too bad you can't bring your Chows too," continues Aba.

"No point," replies Vincent, "Chows don't socialize. They pay no heed to anybody other than their owners."

"But you are proud of them…" Aba hastens to add, "and of your kids too, you must be. Last time at Yung Kee, that was your daughter who was lunching with you, wasn't it? And afterwards she was driving you straight to the airport to catch your flight. I envy you your dutiful children!"

"And I yours. Fine kids," says Vincent politely, "But not as cute as your Chocolate!"

He's frank! I like him.

The dog lovers prattle on.

Vincent takes out his mobile to show Aba pictures of his

two beloved Chow Chows, one brown and one white.

In the meantime, Maggie, Vincent's wife, also comes over to chat with Mimi.

"Phoebus is not joining you this time?" she asks, "He's a splendid young man! You must be proud of your son."

"To be frank with you," Mimi answers, "I am more proud of Chocolate."

After suitably commending the beautiful Chows shown on Vincent's mobile, by now Aba is taking his turn, having his own back, showing Vincent the screen saver on his mobile: a picture of me in brilliant sunlight at Tai Mei Tuk, on the embankment of the Plover Cove Reservoir.

"It was taken after we finished last year's SPCA dogs walkathon, and were riding cycle rickshaws on the embankment there. The sun was shining gloriously so I managed to get a rare shot of Chocolate with his features clearly shown!" Aba relates with relish.

I must admit I enjoyed that occasion too, better than this year's walkathon, also fund-raising for the SPCA but at Hong Kong Disneyland. Here they used only half the path for the walkathon with the other half reserved for visitors to the theme park. It was just too cramped for so many walkers, two- and four-legged together.

While Aba is telling Vincent about the walkathons, Mimi is not to be outmatched. She takes out from her handbag the digital camera with the extra large monitor to show Maggie video recordings of me.

"Wow!" exclaims Maggie, "I've never seen such a large monitor on a digital camera!"

"It's four-inch," narrates Mimi, "So helpful for presbyopic eyes at my age. This gadget is really handy. But I run out of gigs – 'gigabytes', I believe that's what they're called – very quickly on trips abroad. Every time that happens, I have to delete something to make room for new shots, and it saves more room to delete videos than stills, so

I practically deleted all the videos stored in this thing when I was at that botanical garden in Victoria, Canada with all the lovely flowers last summer – all except videos of Chocolate."

And she proceeds to show these videos of me to Maggie, giving a running commentary at the same time.

"That's the SPCA Fun Day last Christmas at Dogs' Park on the waterfront two blocks from here. We entered Chocolate for the obstacle race. Along with his cousins Bobby and Happy, the bichon frises belonging to my younger sister Apple – you remember her?... Bobby was first runner-up…. See? That's Chocolate starting, with me leading him doing that zigzag run round that line of posts…. And his Dad's shooting this video but his hand was so unsteady…. That's Chocolate running through that cloth tunnel, lured by my throwing the rubber ball through it…. That's Chocolate leaping on that block of wood and down again…. That's where he lost time – because he's too quick and bypassed that tyre hanging there…. And then I made him jump through it but he did it the wrong way round jumping back away from the finish and had to do it the right way round again…. So he ended up co-third with Bean Bean, another toy poodle – apricot colour – that we met there at Dogs' Park…. This is all of them on the winners stand…."

While Mimi is button-holing Maggie with this exclusive silent movie preview, Aba is also doing his share by playing another video footage on his mobile for Vincent to view.

"That's the walkathon at Tai Tam Country Park last November for raising funds for the Society for Abandoned Animals – the stray dog refuge organization. Chocolate entered the talent contest…. See, he's standing up to give the wife high ten…. See how he can stand bolt upright with a straight back…. This is him playing dead…. And this is him doing roll-over…. And this is him jumping through the hoop that the wife formed with her arms…. See how he jumped again and again at her command through the hoop…. 'Jump!', and he jumped once again…. 'Jump!', and again… and again… See?... as if he ran on batteries…. Up until the judges – that TV star and that pop singer – took pity on him and asked her to stop…. And they gave him first prize…. See, here they are presenting the trophy, that's a pet pram…. Just the skeleton and wheels of a pram and you've got to put a pet bag on it as seat…. Nowadays Lena pushes Chocolate in this pram downstairs for walks, just to show off to the neighbours… and the lads next door keep asking if they can adopt him…."

Lena showing off? Well, not more than Aba and Mimi are doing right now. I recall Mimi admitting her vain-glory to Aba privately. "We seem to be reliving our early parenthood times, when we took Phoebe to a piano showroom, so she could play Ginastera's *Toccata* there at lightning speed, and outshine the other kids brought by their parents to show off their skills, who could only play that easy stock-in-trade piece, *Für Elise*!"

I am reminded of this while Aba and Mimi are separately showing off to Vincent and Maggie. At last the couple had had enough of my glamour stories and hurried back to their table on some excuse, leaving me to resume my meditation.

They are two model couples from Ricci Hall, where Aba and Vincent were hall-mates for three years in their undergraduate days at HKU. Each was already going steady with their future wives, Mimi and Maggie respectively. Maggie was Vincent's classmate in the History Department, while Aba had been dating Mimi since the Sixth Form.

The only time they were not a foursome on a night out was when Vincent's father barged in. – It was a hilarious anecdote that Aba kept repeating. – A successful businessman, Vincent' father used to tell his son Vincent that being a real macho man meant drinking, swearing and womanizing. On that occasion he was in festive mood and brought along three dance hostesses – in those days, dance hostesses were a sort of rich man's Suzie Wong – from the famous Tonnochy Dance Hall to a night club to intercept Vincent. But Vincent had Maggie with him already, so there were two chicks to spare. Vincent promptly summoned two hall-mates to make the octet. The resulting scenario included Vincent's dad hugging one hostess, while the two penniless Riccians were uncomfortably faced with the two other pros. The pros knew full well who was footing the bill and who were hangers-on, and visibly showed their impatience. One Riccian was at least tall and handsome. Aba, on the other hand, was doubly discomfited, being in shirt sleeves only, and facing a partner dressed in an elegant cheongsam and who was two heads taller.

After sitting and drinking in awkward silence for a while, Aba's partner teasingly challenged him, "Little boy, have you got the guts to dance with me?"

Taking up the challenge, Aba at once regretted doing so. The difference in stature between himself and the woman was highlighted even more on the dance floor, where it turned out his partner was truly a professional and danced superbly opposite him, who was all big toes.

All the while Maggie and Vincent had hysterics as spectators!

After graduation and moving out of Ricci Hall, Aba and Vincent pursued different careers. Although both started as civil servants, they were in different departments. Their paths crossed a few times only after they each got married. In time, Vincent became a businessman and started his own enterprise. The two couples met again at a reunion, a decade ago, held at a third Riccian's mansion – the same tall and handsome one as in the gratis dance-hostess incident.

Then shortly after that, Maggie ran into Phoebus by chance at the Times Square mall. She noticed Phoebus playing the piano there, surrounded by a large crowd. Being short-sighted, she came closer to have a better look, and was greatly surprised, as well as impressed, to find that there was no music-sheet on the piano stand.

"What? You are playing from memory?" The piece was the *Heroic Polonaise.*

Only when they started chatting did Maggie finally learn that Phoebus was Aba's son.

Next they met again at the wedding banquet of Apple's daughter, Mimi's niece. Both Aba and Vincent made speeches on stage that evening. Aba was the bride's uncle, while Vincent was godfather of the bridegroom. Small world!

And the old friends are now fellow caninophiles.

Both are proud of their pets. Only Aba and Mimi are much more eager to exhibit that fact than Vincent and Maggie.

6.   If Food be the Music of Love, Prey on

"Tell me frankly," begins Mimi – whenever she opens her speech with these words Aba will be on the alert to be particularly cautious with his response – "Are we too eager to show off and so we scare them off?"

"Perhaps you're right," Aba replies carefully. "But we ARE proud of Chocolate. That's the gospel-truth. So why worry?"

The discussion comes to a precipitate end when the hot dishes arrive. Let me see – meaning by that the use of a different sensory faculty – ... hmm ... bean sprouts fried with black mushrooms....

"Fried bean sprouts with mushrooms," announces the waiter, confirming my inference, as he puts that dish down.

The other dish is more complicated. What have we here? Heavily seasoned minced pork, minced chili- peppers, and... hmm... bean-flour noodles (like vermicelli but transparent). Odd combination! What's this dish called?

"Ants climbing the tree," the waiter gives the answer to my mental question. What an even odder name for a dish! I thought only the French eat ants. So there's a Shanghai ant dish too, but with no ants in it at all!

As Aba and Mimi set to, I very much wish to continue to reminisce about this afternoon's merriment at Dogs' Park, which induced me to have that colourful dream earlier. But my brain keeps receiving signals from my nose, picking up those porky ants climbing that chili-pepper and bean-starch noodle tree....

For a poodle, food is always top priority over play. Hence, aroused by the aroma of their dishes, my mind wanders to meals instead.

Food, glorious food! It gives me great joy. So does play, of course. So do some other things following behind these top two items but to lesser degrees.

I have always been a very happy dog under Mimi's, Aba's and Lena's care, never lacking in food or fun, fed on kibbles since day one at home, supplemented by occasional – I would say very occasional ... few and far between – rewards of snacks when Mimi, essentially the sole controller of my ration of snacks, orders me to perform tricks and in response I comply and perform to her satisfaction. This is usually in public, showing off to some spectators, be they acquaintances or total strangers, mere passers-by.

I have recently become an even happier dog. Because Mimi has made a momentous decision to give me frozen raw meat instead of kibble as my staple food. First I sampled beef imported from Australia, my Motherland, and after a month's trial, switched to venison from New Zealand. The plan for the future, as Mimi instructed Lena in Hongkongese, i.e. in English primarily for the benefit of Lena but with Cantonese interjections like abbellimenti, "La, Lena, in future ne, one packet beef, then one packet venison, alternate ah ha, you understand ah ma?" On top of two meals a day on these nutriments, I am also fed regularly with at least one bone to chew a day. And, to crown it all, Mimi has bought four deep-frozen lamb chops – shanks, I believe – from the celebrated imported frozen meat store Wo Hing Hong. Lena has defrosted one and steamed it, without adding any seasoning, for me to take every weekend over the past month. So on my lamb chop day of the week, I have my two standard meat meals, plus one lamb chop to last an hour – as opposed to each meat meal that takes me about ten seconds to consume. First I pick off the meat from the lamb chop, which is already extraordinarily gratifying. Then I still have the bone to chew for the rest of the hour! What more can one ask for in life? And this, again as I overheard, is to become a weekend fixture for me.

I well understand why this weighty decision was made. Mimi and I run into Bean Bean and his owners every now and then. Bean Bean was co-second-runner-up with me at the SPCA obstacle race held at Dogs' Park last Christmas. He is a three-year old apricot-colour toy poodle. Always bursting with energy. Also extremely greedy. We met them – Bean Bean and his humans – at Dogs' Park again, early this year, and witnessed how Bean Bean blatantly snatched some stranger's packed lunch. When his owners cornered him, he had already downed the sandwich in one gulp. He was punished: made to sit still until further notice. Small cost to pay for a sandwich lunch! No deterrent at all, if you ask me.

We met them again on Victoria Peak three months later, and Mimi was most impressed to find Bean Bean even more energetic and looking extremely healthy. His owners explained that, on expert advice, they had switched from kibble to a meat diet for him. That's what persuaded Mimi to follow suit. The one drawback is that meat is softer than kibble. Hence the extra bone to give me chewing exercise and strengthen as well as clean my teeth in the process.

It says on the packet of the New Zealand venison that dogs are 99.8 percent wolf! In contrast, the DNA of the wolf's closest wild relative, the coyote, is four percent different, 3.8 percent more distantly related than dogs to the lupine tribe. That provides the rationale for giving dogs a raw meat diet based on that of the grey wolf, to feed their inner wolf! I have no head for this sophisticated theoretical justification. All I know is that I feel more elated and more lively after switching from monotonous kibble to a carnivorous regimen. Mimi's appraisal of the effects of my changed diet is as follows: "Decolorization of fur arrested. Colour stabilized at uniform milk-chocolate hue, with lighter patches on back and tail only. Cheerful and doubly playful. In fact, bordering on hyperactive!"

Furthermore, I still receive my additional treats of snacks every now and then. There is only one snag where snacks are concerned. They make Mimi more demanding. Every time a snack is in the offing she makes me rehearse the tricks I've learned for a longer time and at a greater degree of difficulty.

"Sit. Hand. Next hand. Gimme five. High ten (this means standing on my hind legs and stretching my fore legs straight up in the air). Swing (i.e. standing on my hind legs and spinning round clockwise or counter-clockwise). Sit. Down (meaning lying flat on my stomach). Bang! (whereupon I play dead). Up. Jump!..." And that last command will be repeated again and again, with Mimi either forming the hoop with her arms, or stretching out a leg as a hurdle, as well as raising it higher and higher.

And the hardest trick of all is when at the end of the drill she places the snack in front of me, literally right under my nose, and commands, "Leave it!" And I have to exercise the highest degree of self-control and not touch the coveted snack, sitting still and resisting the temptation, until she eventually commands, "Take it!"

To be honest, I don't mind doing all that – at once impressing all spectators, and earning my snack – provided the snack is of a standard worth the trouble, AND provided also that it agrees with my by now connoisseur's taste! My favourite snack is the chicken liver sausage Rufina ordered from Japan as a gift to me *via* her Godmother – *foie de volaille pour Chocolat*!

But often times Mimi doles out indifferent snacks such as cookies, pretzels and chips. In the case of these, no thanks. I'd rather save my energy for better *hors d'oeuvres*.

Once, after an outing, Mimi left unfinished chicken liver sausage in the convenience bag – the carrier bag in which are kept the paraphernalia for walking me, including water bottle for flushing my wee wee, tissue paper for picking up my poo poo and wiping my butt, the rubber ball for playing fetch in the lift lobby after walking, and the door key. Well, the bag is always deposited on the hall table next to the main door. Knowing what was inside this time, I reached up to the table top, toppled the bag, rummaged in it and finally managed to have a bite of my favourite snack.

"Bad boy!" was Mimi's instant reaction. She drove me out of the sitting room to the balcony, closed the French window, and shut me out there with the potted plants, as my penalty.

I was totally at a loss what I had done wrong. In the normal course of events I would have to do all those tricks at Mimi's command to earn my treat. That's a treat, hard earned with hard labour. So when I seized the chance to get hold of the snack, which was for feeding me and no-one else anyway, by equally hard labour – craning my legs and muzzle to reach that packet – why was it considered a crime, or even a sin? It's not like Bean Bean stealing a human's snack from total strangers, just dog eat dog's!

I knew better and received my punishment quietly, but without learning any lesson. The logic of, "one must beg from one's feeder for snacks and not help oneself," is simply beyond my simple mind. Nevertheless, all's well that ends well. Dogs specialize in Stanislavsky's Method Acting – putting on a piteous facial expression to the most moving degree. Mimi soon relented and, opening the French window of my temporary prison, hugged me in her arms and covered me with kisses while murmuring, "Poor Chocolate! Poor baby."

To complete this treatise on gluttony, the "bone" I am given to chew daily is either a preserved rib with meat morsels clinging on it, which is a snack, or sometimes just a fake bone made of raw hide! My parents are amazed with my exquisite discriminating taste…. I show preference for the more expensive variety of raw hide bone bought in a

Western District pet shop, than the one from the Central supermarket, even though both are made in Thailand and look identical.

I am grateful to Mimi for always having my well-being foremost in mind. Not only in feeding me the best, but also in feeling genuine concern. I remember that night she took me to the 24-hour emergency vet clinic for an X-ray, just to ascertain if I had swallowed her missing earring! (It cost a fortune – the X-ray, I mean, not the earring – and it – the earring, I mean – was found by Lena as soon as we had left.) And that other time when I vomited that shapeless pulp, she was worried to death, until Lena worked out in true CSI style that it was a nylon stocking that I had gulped down earlier.

Back to more pleasant culinary choices. While they enjoy their tree-scaling emmets, I start my own soul-searching. (Perhaps stomach-searching is closer to the truth.) I ask myself in my private brown study the million dollar question. Which do I like best – dining at places where dogs are allowed, like the Stanley promenade brasseries, the Shek O beachside cafés, the Wanchai waterfront San Li Tun rotisseries, the Soho trattorias, the Sai Kung street fast-food stores, and the Happy Valley tram terminus piazza bistros, etcetera; or hidden in the bag just to stay side by side with Aba and Mimi, at places serving humans only?

Naturally my favourite is the Dog Café in the vicinity of this Shanghai restaurant. I have only had two birthday parties so far. My one-year-old party was held at Phoebus's office. It was on a small scale, with my family members only. The candle was blown out, and the birthday cake was cut up and shared, all on my behalf, by the humans! I felt like Buddha or Sun Yat-sen (replacing the Queen), those whose birthdays give others an excuse to enjoy a holiday!

I had my two-year-old birthday party at Dog Café for a

change. An exclusive section was reserved for the purpose. All my canine relatives and friends attended with their humans. There was Roger (Aba's brother) and his wife Emily who insisted on carrying her "easily frightened baby" Snoopy, a thirty-kilogramme husky, in her arms, to her great discomfort and Cousin Snoopy's great humiliation! I was positive he'd rather have his feet on the floor, but she was true to character in being overprotective of her kids, human and canine alike. On Mimi's side, Apple brought Bobby and Happy, and Veronica, the youngest sister brought Cosy the Yorkshire terrier. Happy was two, slightly older than me. Bobby was three and Cosy was six. All were my elder cousins. Our version of the eternal triangle was Cousin Happy teasing me, luring me into running around and playing with her, and then Cousin Bobby her protector would bark fiercely at me as if I were bullying Cousin Happy. Cousin Cosy had been my partner at my first photo-studio session. Like Cousin Snoopy, she had always been house-bound and was consequently unsociable and shy. Rufina was there too with her Shih Tzu, Lucky Mui (the name means "Lucky Girlie"), the dragon of the party!

This Café is a lovely place. The owner herself keeps three red toy poodles, Fan Shü (Potato), Fan Gua (Pumpkin) and Fan Gung (At Work), who work there as resident Public Relations Officers. Here we can all run around freely and mingle with other customers, humans and dogs alike. And by doing the right things one gets free treats occasionally from total strangers!

"We never got McDonald's birthday parties when we were small," protested Fabian sourly.

"But then McDonald's is not as much fun as this!" observed Phoebus.

This time the birthday cake was for dogs and we shared it in complete harmony.

However, it is not always fun at places where you can

take dogs. Unlike the Dog Café which has a special license to operate upstairs and indoors, in other places it always involves taking an outdoor table, and either sweating in the hot summer or shivering in the cold and windy winter. Moreover, most places do not allow us to occupy seats, and this means being on the lead, tied to a chair-leg, with nowhere to go and nothing to do throughout the humans repast.

Even my latest Valentine's Day dinner was not without a setback. Mimi and Aba dressed me up in tails, complete with shirt front and bow tie (but mercifully no trousers). They even bought a long stemmed red rose for me to take along as a Valentine's Day token. Thus prepared, we picked up Rufina and Lucky Mui. The latter was a ten-year-old abandoned Shih Tzu, blind in one eye. Most likely she had suffered untold tortures at certain human hands, and probably at children's hands too, and as a result she had a very limited sense of security, barking at anybody drawing near within her blurred sight, in particular children for whom she proffered the fiercest yapping.

Rufina adopted her out of pity, gave her unprecedented kindness in appreciation of the company she gave her, and always dressed her up beautifully like a princess. Being my date that night, she was in evening dress to match my tails: bare shoulders with shoulder straps and all that black lace accentuating her white fur. Too bad I was neutered so there was no chemistry at all between us. – Remember that peanut-shaped chew toy from my infant days? That is now my "wife," which I occasionally mount, to do push-ups on involuntarily, even subconsciously. (I usually fall asleep in the process.) – Nor was she impressed by the long-stemmed rose.

Nonetheless, the two of us were made to sit together, shoulder to shoulder, with the long-stemmed rose in the foreground, for a photograph to record the occasion. Never was there a more wooden Valentine pair!

While we were settling down at our reserved table at the Thai restaurant at San Li Tun – a commercial building podium on the Wanchai waterfront where restaurants have both indoor and outdoor sections – the party at the next table, who were already having their desserts, complained about having non-human neighbours thrust upon them. The *maître d'* politely sought our consent to move to a table further away. But the obnoxious man, a gigolo by his looks, kept on grumbling. The *maître d'* raised his voice for us to hear, "They've moved, haven't they? That's all I'll do to my customers!"

By then, Aba was incensed and uncharacteristically raised his voice for that whiner's benefit, "I made an advance booking. I paid a higher price for the after-eight slot. All for my Chocolate's Valentine Date! Chocolate is a prince to me! Miserable creature, loveless even on Valentine's Day, that he begrudges us our delightful party! No, I am not angry with him. In fact I pity him!"

That was the first time I heard Aba confer on me the title of "prince," the same as accorded to Phoebus! It reminds me of an art and culture web-magazine's interview of Aba. When asked if he felt embarrassed that his son was called, "Prince of the Piano," he replied, "Embarrassed? Why should I be? It's fine by me. 'Cause if he's a prince, that makes me a king!"

After dinner, we found the outdoor tables of the French rotisserie next door all occupied by dogs and owners. A very convivial Valentine's party for dog lovers and lover dogs! Wish we had made our booking there instead.

7.   Happy Life with a Lovely Dog

Retrieving my selective memories of a gourmet's glee, I must admit that Aba was equally selective in showing Vincent video shots only of my glory and victory. He has many snapshots of me stored in his mobile, which – I mean the mobile phone – was a gift from Phoebe on her last homecoming in May 2008.

The picture I like best myself is however one Aba feels abashed to show. It was taken on a rainy day when outdoor activity was out of the question. So we went to EMax, the shopping mall at Kowloon Bay that used to be a trade exhibition centre, and which is still partly used for that purpose. There is a whole floor entitled Pet Max and dedicated to pet shops.

It is therefore the one mall in Hong Kong where pets are actually welcome, provided they are carried in bags or in shopping trolleys supplied by the mall on floors other than Pet Max. It even has one elevator devoted to transporting pets. It is a favourite haunt for us in bad weather. Mimi can satisfy her feminine shopping instinct, even if just by window-shopping. If the rain stops there is a roof garden with artificial turf, pet-slides and a splashing-pool for pets to play in.

On that visit, one pet shop was promoting and displaying a certain brand of organic dog food in trays on a table, with a sign saying, "Sampling welcome". Aba used the mobile to take a snapshot of me standing bolt upright on my hind legs, facing that sign and the food trays, my tongue hanging out!

As my parents had learned from bitter experience early on, it was beyond their capability to take good shots of me, what with my uniformly dark features. And hence, when I was only six months old, Mimi took me to a pet studio, the word "Paradise" in its name aptly indicating the nature of the surroundings. The proprietor-cum-photographer was an affectionate dog-owner himself. His own Yorkshire terriers, Ice and Cream, served as models in the studio's promotional pictures, prominently displayed in light-boxes. He genuinely enjoyed taking pictures of dogs and capturing their best moments. They had several pet portrait packages to choose from. Mimi picked a reasonably-priced one for two dogs and no humans, which included one album of some four dozen best pictures, selected from a hundred taken, plus a CD of the same stills.

My partner for this my first studio session was Cousin Cosy, a Yorkshire terrier like the photographer's Ice and Cream, four years older than me, and a girl. The session took one whole afternoon. Several backdrops were used, including a lawn bestrewn with flowers, every colour of the rainbow – so that's the inspiration for my dream! – There was a blue sky with white clouds and green trees. There was a snow-capped mountain against which we rode in a colourful toy convertible buggy. (The so-called "convertible" was actually a car with no roof; it wouldn't really "convert"). And there was a classy garden with exquisite horticulture, white picket fences and a dainty white chair. We had several changes of costume. I was chiefly in sporty white tee shirt and jeans; while Cousin Cosy was in white blouse and denim skirt.

That was my first decent album, which now sits at the bottom of the coffee table in the sitting room, for all callers to view and admire. I was just a baby, and made a lot of funny faces, my tongue hanging out or curling upwards half of the time. Cousin Cosy, of fairer hair and more lady-like, was prettier and much more presentable.

My second studio session turned out to be a happy family reunion!

That was in May 2008.

Phoebe had just finished a trip to Japan and came back to Hong Kong for a week's short stay before returning to

Sydney. She brought a Mother's Day present for Mimi – I've forgotten what it was – must have been something totally uninteresting to me. But I distinctly recall that she bought that mobile as an advance Fathers' Day present for Aba. Naturally I remember this, as I am a beneficiary of that present's functions.

Perhaps prompted by the camera and video-recording functions of this new toy of Aba's, Mimi had the sudden idea to have a family photo taken when everybody was here, a rare situation these days. The last time a family photo was taken dated back to 1997.

Phoebe had to fly in a couple of days' time. It was too short notice to book a studio for humans. So we settled for my pet studio *paradiso* once again. The package opted for this time was naturally more expensive than that of my own first album, but much cheaper even so than a studio for humans. It included enlarged family portraits in oil painting form (frames not included), an album of fifty pictures from two hundred shots taken, and two discs – one CD of stills and one DVD slide-show with background music. The catch was that the package covered one dog and two humans, extra humans individually charged, but still it came to only a tenth of the human-only studio price.

We had a great time, spending a total of three hours at the studio. That was not counting Danielle, Phoebus's girlfriend, who had to catch a ferry to Macau and went to the studio ahead of the family to have a dozen pictures taken with me first, with a background of palm trees and sunny beach.

We then had different combinations of family members, but with me featuring in every shot. There were whole-family shots with a cosy family room background complete with grandfather clock and high-backed leather arm-chair, and me either in Mimi's arms, or sitting on a white sheepskin rug in the foreground in sharp contrast to my complexion. Then I had small group photos, some with the parents, others with the children. Next I posed with each of them in turn (Aba calls these, "duet photos"), including with Lena. I had changes of costume as before. I had a red tee shirt, the tails which Mimi eventually bought and that I wore again on Valentine's Day 2009 – grey silk with black lapels, white shirt front and black bow tie – and thirdly, my birthday suit with only a white scarf around my neck.

I also had some solo shots in tails. It was with these that Aba later started my blog.

Phoebe was dressed in an orange blouse. My red tee shirt complemented her perfectly. I enjoyed teasing her, and our duet pictures are full of dynamism – her pink cheeks matching my pinker tongue.

Fabian made funny faces, sticking his tongue out and growling at me. I curled up my tongue in return; something no human could do as well.

Phoebus had on his white polo shirt and jeans with black jacket. Seeing me in tails, he borrowed a dog's bow tie from the shop and wore it to match my formal dress.

The photographer warned us before he began, "I'm only watching Chocolate to capture him at his best. You others look sharp at all times to look your best. I won't bother about you."

In the event we all came out looking marvellous.

Mimi was glamorous as ever in her elegant white-knit top, black slacks and shiny silver shoes like Cinderella's glass slippers.

Even Aba changed his top, wearing both a childish Disney tee shirt in red and blue with a white Mickey Mouse stamped on it, and also a Burberry shirt, for two series, one with sporty and the other with a sophisticated look respectively.

Later, when he took the finished album to his office and showed it to his colleagues, the consensus comment was,

"Just looking at the album, one can tell this is a very happy family!"

The studio proprietor apparently thought so too: the DVD and album were both given the engraved title: "Happy Life with Lovely Dog – Chocolate & Family".

It was really a happy occasion with the whole family reunited. It was the second time I saw Phoebe. She had been back once before when I had newly joined the family, on a previous brief passing-by visit. This time we had a whole week together and I grew to love this Big Sister very much. Like me, she was eternally cheerful, always wearing a smiling face. The difference was that hers was a pretty girlish face, while mine was a silly boyish grin. Nevertheless, we two got along just fine!

After the salon session, we had dinner before Phoebe left for Australia. It was at the French rotisserie at San Li Tun (next door to the Thai place where I later had my Valentine's Day date, the one I've already told you about).

That dinner with Phoebe was a memorable reunion, enjoyed at an alfresco table for six with candle-light. Only Lena was missing, having gone home first to hold the fort.

I was assigned my own seat, with my bag as cushion. A juicy bone was my share of the dinner.

In between munching, I caught the following most quotable outpourings that night from individual family members' hearts.

"It's the undeniable truth that Chocolate has brought happiness to the household." (Mimi)

"Don't say Chocolate is a blessed puppy to have loving owners like us. The fact is we are a blessed family to have such a blessing in Chocolate!" (Aba)

"I am very dejected and cross after a hard day's work, facing demanding and even unreasonable clients. Then I arrive home and Chocolate comes rushing to greet me licking my face all wet; and at once I forget all my troubles!" (Phoebus)

"He makes me relive all those happy days of bringing up my babies. You all grew up so quickly, and we were too busy then to have the chance really to relish the joy of parenthood! Now I am repeating my bad guy role of my younger days, doing the same thankless jobs as I did for you: enforcing discipline, combing his fur, brushing his teeth and cleaning his eyes and ears, plucking hair from inside his ears. Naturally he loathes all this! But what else can a mother do?" (Mimi)

"We've been a family scattered asunder all over the globe. Not only geographically. We each live in our own small world of work and work and work and little else. Chocolate has become a wonderful cohesive force. Now we are a cohesive happy family having a reunion dinner after a family photo- taking session. Everyone loves Chocolate!" (Fabian)

"Everyone loves staying home with Chocolate. Lena smiles all day long nowadays. I myself genuinely miss Chocolate on Sundays when I wake up and find he's gone out with Mimi and Aba." (Phoebus)

"I gave up my column in the newspaper when I wrote that article on Chocolate, and the cultural page editor censored it, ruling that it had nothing to do with culture. But I never regret its loss. It was worth making a sacrifice for Chocolate, and not having a column to write gives me more free time to spend with him." (Aba)

"When Aba and I have a fight, Chocolate is very upset. He tugs us apart with his teeth and gives us that earnest pleading look, making us both feel so guilty for upsetting him that we soon make up. A tug of peace, that's what it is!" (Mimi)

"I'm the only one of the family still living abroad. This time I'll be taking these discs and album back with me, so I can go on sharing all our happy days together!" (Phoebe)…

Still, I miss you, Big Sister!

"Goodbye!"....

I am abruptly recalled from reminiscence to the present, when Vincent and Maggie come over again, this time to take their leave.

8. Whoopees and Whincs

"Let's have a get-together some day, our two families," proposes Vincent.

Sounds to me a polite parting proposition, made with a view to getting away quickly without being subjected again to the same Chocolate parade. Aba, however, interprets it differently.

"Good idea," he replies enthusiastically, "Let's pick a Sunday and have an outing, our two families, four-legged members included!"

"Yes," concurs Mimi excitedly, "Bring your kids and your Chows. We can walk up Hatton Road to the Peak. Chocolate loves the piazza outside Peak Galleria. Even more than Dogs' Park…."

Her words prompt me to proceed to recollections of my weekend routines.

I recognise weekdays as working days when all family members get into formal dress – suit and tie for the men, much greater diversity for Mimi – and go to work in the morning, leaving me with Lena at home.

Saturday is a variable day. Sometimes Fabian gets up as late as Phoebus does, but they always go out and stay out until very late at night, mostly even later than usual. As for Mimi, more often than not she goes to school the same as on weekdays but dresses even more gorgeously for the special occasions that happen on Saturdays, PTA meetings, School Cultural Days, etcetera. And Aba, he is supposed to keep a five-day working week but he declares Saturday is the best day for working quietly in the office with no disturbance. Later in the day he and Mimi rendezvous for a night out, mostly to watch a play. And in consequence I am still oftentimes left alone, even more alone or alone longer, on Saturdays.

Except, that is, when Aba is in holiday mood. In this case

he will skip the office and take me out on Saturday morning and/or afternoon. Most probably for a long walk up Hatton Road to the Peak. There is a midway stop at the picnic area named Pinewood Battery, an old shore-battery site where cannon once commanded the western harbour entrance, but where now there are only ruins of bunkers, overgrown with South China pines and a stretch of turf. Aba plays fetch with me there, throwing a colourful rubber ball that squeaks on being squeezed, for me to catch. He says it is at best playing "catch," not "fetch," because after I dash forward and catch the ball, I never bring it back to the thrower. Instead I hang on to the ball, squeezed between my teeth and squeaking, run back towards Aba but, just missing him, sashay past him and hide in the bush where the turf ends.

Aba chides me for it with his words. "Bad boy, Chocolate!" Not a grain of truth in it! I can tell from the expressions on his face that he is most gratified to see that I am enjoying myself.

"The way Chocolate runs, fore and hind legs alternately off the ground, ears and tail thrown up in the air – that's a beautiful picture of pure happiness!" That's how Aba describes me to Mimi.

I will usually be so happy that I start lying supine on the turf and rolling this way and that, collecting blades of grass and twigs on my fur. That most probably will bring to an end our rollicking time at Pinewood Battery.

Then we continue the ascent. In the cold season I walk the whole way freely off the leash. The freedom symbolizes Aba's trust and my impeccable conduct report card. In summer, on especially warm and sunny days, when I drag my feet a little and hang my tongue out panting, Aba thoughtfully holds me in his arms as if carrying a baby, for at least an unsheltered stretch of the path. Mercifully the way to the Peak is over ninety percent tree-lined and shaded at all hours.

Hatton Road ends where it joins Lugard Road, which, together with Harlech Road, forms a full circle around the Victoria Peak area. It constitutes a favourite leaf-shaded walk for Hong Kong citizens, with its panoramic views of Victoria Harbour, Hong Kong Island north, Kowloon and Hong Kong Island south. After the climb, we walk with relative ease along this level stretch of Lugard Road until we reach Peak Galleria, the mall next to the Peak Tram Terminus, with a piazza outside its entrance where tourists converge.

From habit, weekend after weekend, this has become my alfresco studio. I am used to being admired by passers-by who first give a surprised exclamation – not expecting to find that I am not a toy teddy bear – saying either, "Is he real?" or, "Look, he's moving!"

That's why Mimi concludes that I love this piazza even more than Dogs' Park, "At Dogs' Park he's one of the crowd. At the Peak there are fewer dogs and he always stands out."

"And he prefers the company of humans to dogs," adds Aba, "since he sees himself as a human being."

That's what they think. Far be it from me to correct them. What I know is that Aba is the one who definitely prefers the Peak piazza to Dogs' Park. He confesses as much privately to his sons.

"At my age I don't get many pretty young things in hot pants and low cut tops, speaking English or Putonghua, sticking their faces next to mine posing for pictures, except when I have Chocolate in my arms! Them – I mean those – tourists (a rare ungrammatical slip by Aba, as far as I can make out) simply adore him!"

And the place is indeed an outdoor photo studio. I have grown accustomed to being asked to pose for snapshots with tourists, so much so that I automatically sit still whenever someone stands or crouches next to me facing a camera. They commend me for behaving virtually as a professional model!

Then, after tarrying for long enough on the piazza, playing "catch" interspersed with posing for pictures, we retrace the same route downhill and back home.

We repeat the same programme on Sunday mornings. The only differences are we have Mimi joining us, and she and Aba have a meal at the Peak. If we start early they have breakfast at the French café on the piazza. If not, they have a dim sum lunch at the Chinese restaurant. In either case we occupy an outdoor table for my sake.

Yes, I admit to a little vanity and weakness for the Peak piazza. If we are there early enough – after breakfast (and sometimes even before) – we will go on up Mount Austin Road to the very top. There is another park there, only this one is much larger and divided into several tiered levels, and it is open to dogs. We can play fetch – I mean catch –on the wide lawns there to our hearts content. Other families have picnics there and the kids will always play with me happily and part with me sadly.

I pause in my day-dream to register the present situation update. Vincent and Maggie have, as predicted, retreated hurriedly, before (and therefore avoiding) making any further commitment. Who in sound mind would expect one as plump as Vincent to join a hike up Hatton Road?

It is difficult to visualize Vincent the young Riccian, playing forward (I am not sure whether he played on the Right or Left Wing) in the Ricci Hall soccer team, lean as a beanstalk, with an explosive short distance dash at breakneck speed. Breakneck is literally true, according to Aba. For Vincent ran with long strides and, at each stride, his back foot kicked up so high that it seemed to reach the back of his head! Hence his nickname at the time, "The man who kicks his own nape".

Too many flashbacks!

I must return to this afternoon's fun at Dogs' Park as I

have been planning to do all this time but for all these interruptions. Dogs' Park is another favourite haunt of ours on Sundays, on winter mornings when it is overcast, or at dusk. It is just too warm and the sun too unbearable most of the day in summer months. Before the Government proceeds with the Wanchai bypass project to ease the traffic on the waterfront highway, this stretch, formally entitled the Wanchai Waterfront Promenade, has been temporarily converted into a Dogs' Park, a narrow strip equally divided into two halves, both having a wooden planked deck on the water side and a lawn with bushes on the inland side.

Mimi and Aba take me where dogs and their owners gather, with a view to giving me an opportunity to socialize, me with fellow canines and they themselves with fellow owners. And we also play catch there.

It does not quite work out as they wish.

"Chocolate is preoccupied with the ball only and doesn't socialize at all!" claims Mimi.

"How can he?" Aba defends me. "When we throw the ball the other dogs run after it, and Chocolate has no possessive spirit in him. He always lets others have the ball without putting up any fight or racing for it."

They just don't get it, in sharing we socialize! Dogs fight over a bone, never a ball.

We played catch there, at Dogs' Park, this afternoon before coming here. And I had great fun. Sunday, sweet Sunday! I dreamed of it afterwards on the way here – Sunday sweet....

"Sweets are on the house," Mr Zang's voice rouses me from sweet memories. "It's mini dumplings, no filling, just glutinous rice paste, in sweet soup of wine press lees."

Smells like that too. Rice paste in rice wine dregs.

He deposits the two mini-bowls of sweets and discreetly withdraws to leave the couple to partake of this last course.

I resume my equally, if not more, sweet RAM (I believe

it stands for "random access memory") of my Sunday sundaes, figuratively speaking. There are more outing options in the colder months and less risk of sunstroke. We may go up Wong Nai Chung Gap to Hong Kong Parkview, where the Tai Tam Reservoir Country Park hiking route begins. Here also I get to walk freely all the way, sometimes up Mount Parker Road and then down to Quarry Bay, other times to Tai Tam Reservoir and on to Stanley. We have also taken longer journeys in the family car, with Mimi driving and Aba navigating, to the New Territories and different places there. To Tai Mei Tuk, where we walk or ride in cycle rickshaws (they pedal and I sit in the front seat to receive people's admiration) on the Plover Cove Reservoir embankment. To Sai Kung where we join the parade of dogs – that's what most owners do there: parading their dogs – along the waterfront square and park. Alternatively, we drive to Shek O beach – not the main beach which bans dogs as all other public beaches do – but the deserted one with no life-guards and where there's a pub that welcomes dog-owners, and where dogs can stroll on the beach and have a dip.

All these places offer beautiful scenery which, I am sorry to say, is lost to me whose interest is on playing rather than admiring the sights of nature.

Aba also laments often that he would have written travelogues but for his lack of botanical knowledge: "It looks silly if I keep writing about a scenic spot full of trees I cannot name and flowers I do not recognize."

On rainy days, an indoor shopping mall is the only answer. And EMax, with its Pet Max floor – entirely dedicated to pet shops – is one of only two spots where I can play catch indoors. The lift lobby at home downstairs is the other one. But I think I've told you that already.

But come rain come shine, we can always go to Park Island, the housing estate that is truly a dog's paradise. The other name for Park Island is Ma Wan Island. And a theme park with a life-sized Noah's Ark is going to open there. (By the time you read this, it may already be open.) Apple moved there from Happy Valley to give Bobby and Happy a dream home after their Happy Valley neighbours complained about barking. We go there on the ferry, where I can openly ride in the front row without hiding in a bag. There is a beach for dogs, a park for dogs, and walks throughout the estate and the square are all full of freely strolling dogs. I remember our first visit to Apple's place. When we were waiting for the elevator in the lobby, the caretaker approached us politely and asked us to let a resident and his huge mastiff take the first lift first. First time I witnessed a building giving priority treatment to canines! And inside the lift, there is a sign giving advice to humans on how to get along with dogs, especially in a restricted space such as inside a lift.

While I am dreaming of Park Island, Mimi and Aba have finished their dessert and are chatting.

"It's been a happy day, hasn't it?" Aba begins, "Great fun this afternoon at Dogs' Park!"

"Only it's a pity Chocolate paid no attention at all to the other dogs, just focused on chasing his ball, and hiding it in the bush. Every time he disappeared into the bush he made me so worried!" Mimi shook her head in exasperation.

"But you got him out in no time. You always make him play catch only on the planked stretch."

"Yes, because I don't want him to be stung by cattle tick again!" exclaims Mimi, "He scares me to death every time he rolls about on a stretch of grass, let alone vanishing into a bush!"

I know. We both have heart-rending memories of my near demise, shortly after my first birthday party. I was bitten by a cattle tick, as the vet diagnosed it. They're always found in grass or bushes newly dampened from rain.

Cattle tick, as the name forewarns, can bleed a whole steer dry. Veritable vampires! I went all ashy pale in all my furless parts: belly and gums inside my mouth. And I lay lifelessly inert, all energy seemingly sapped from my body. Mimi wept day and night for that whole week when my life was hanging by a thread. Until the vet finally declared I was saved!

"Just as heart-stopping and nail-biting," reminisced Aba, "As when Phoebus had acute appendicitis at two, or cut his upper lip open when he fell on the metal track at the base of the French window …"

"Or when Fabian had tonsillitis," joined in Mimi.

I don't want to recall that dreadful ordeal. No, Sir. Not ever!

Nor do I want to be reminded of my parents' prolonged absence on overseas trips in the summer or winter vacations. Every time I saw Lena taking the suitcases down from the cupboard shelves I started a period of depression. I would pine away in their empty bed most of the day throughout the time of their absences until the exhilaration of their return.

Let me reminisce instead about the fun this afternoon at Dogs' Park, as I have been wanting to do all this time.

Dogs' Park is a rare blessing, coming from the Government, and too good to last! All the more reason to make the most of it before it is closed down by the end of the year.

The Government official who made Dogs' Park happen is another former fellow-Riccian. He is not a dog owner. I remember Aba talking to him at a Chinese New Year party this official gave at his house.

"You should keep a dog. Great friend for a guy. You work like a dog all day and you come home to find he's always there to welcome you home!"

The official's wife rebutted, "Well, *I* am always there to

welcome him home!"

"Yes, but do you lick your husband all over his face to show your welcome?"....

Why do I keep digressing in my recollections? Focus on the fun at Dogs' Park just now, you son of a caninus femininus! (Oh, excuse my Latin!)

We played fetch...or catch.

Such great fun that I was dreaming of it even when arriving here.

Mimi hurled the multi-coloured squeaky ball far and high. – She bought a whole lot of these balls at Sai Kung. They can't be found anywhere else. – I darted forward and caught it with my teeth. Then I did what Mimi identified, from her yoga lessons, as "Salutation to the Moon," my head down between my fore-paws, my chest touching the ground, my back arched, and my croup sticking high up in the air. I always do this as soon as I have caught the ball, an invitation to my playmate to share my playfulness, a sort of "on your marks" posture, ready to dash off when the other party moves.

I also do it as a stretching exercise when I get up after a night's sleep, and when I get out of the bag after being zipped up inside it for a long while, just as I am going to do once outside this place and this bag....

Mimi responded to my Salutation by heading straight for me, a hand stretched out to snatch my ball.

Then I hared towards the bush. Whereupon Mimi curtly stopped me by the command I was taught at obedience school, "Uh-uh!"...

"Ahem...."

I am again distracted.

It is the *maître d'*, Mr Zang, bringing the bill.

Chocolate's Brown Study in the Bag

9. Happiness is...

Aba reaches for his wallet. Mimi stops him.

"Uh-uh. Let me do it." And she takes out her credit card which is in fact a supplementary card of Aba's.

She does this all the time, saying Aba, being a man, is prone to be too liberal with his tips.

"We've got to be more careful with spending," she once elaborated. "We will retire one of these days. And while we don't mind adjusting our standard of living, I don't want to have to lower Chocolate's. A woman is not supposed to tip and there's no loss of face if I sign the chit."

"I understand," Aba nodded. "Like when you started dyeing my hair at home instead of my having it done at a barber shop, so we can save that money for Chocolate's grooming by the Japanese stylist. And these days I don't dye my hair at all. White hair becomes me."

While she is signing the bill, Mr Zang keeps bowing, "Thank you. We look forward to your patronage again.... Bring your sons next time. Such fine lads!... And HE's most welcome too...."

And at this point, Mr Zang casts a sidelong glance, just as Aba did, at me in my bag.

He goes on, "As long as he stays so well-behaved in the bag it doesn't matter. You understand our difficulty.... Food and Hygiene Department Inspectors, customers who may complain, and all that...."

So he knows after all!

"So the cat's out of the bag!" sighs Mimi as Mr Zang withdraws.

But I am not a cat, Mimi! I am Chocolate, your last born!

I know I am only one of your children, albeit the last born.

But I KNOW you think the world of me!

It won't be long now when we will be out in the street,

and I will be let out of the bag, and will stretch myself with my "Salutation to the Moon"....

My alertness is consequently lowered, and I start dozing off again. Darkness sets in....

My colourful dream, of the ball flying over the lawn bestrewn with flowers under the sunlit sky, is just beginning, when all of a sudden...

"Tell me frankly," starts Mimi, and Aba and I both activate our alarm signal, as she continues, "Are we in fact merely two doting old fools overindulging Chocolate?"

Now what does that mean, Mimi?

"Why?" Aba asks in return, warily, "You mean we scrimp and save for his sake? We are not doing more for him than what we did for our children."

And Mimi, I'm your last born!

"But he's only a dog!"

Oh, Mimi! Coming from you....This really hurts!

"Oh, no," Aba starts his rhetoric – and when he does there's no stopping him, not all the uh-uhs in the world. "Remember? I've said he's a blessing. He's an angel of happiness sent by Heaven, to bring happiness to our family!"

Thanks, Aba!

"You always say such hollow-sounding things which have no meaning in real life." Mimi assumes the role of devil's advocate. "You called Phoebe that too when she was born."

Oh! So I am not the first to be called that.

"And I mean it every time. So we have more than one angel of happiness in the family. Isn't that just great? Count your blessings!"

Quite right. We dogs are good at that. Mimi, you should follow our example and start counting.

"And what is a blessing?" Mimi presses on, "What is happiness?"

"What do you mean?"

You've lost me too, Mimi. You begin to sound like a philosopher. – You see, I remember Aba describing to his sons what he learned in his first year philosophy course, that philosophers only raise questions, without bothering to provide answers.

"Well, just for argument's sake" – it was Mimi's turn to start her rhetoric – "Not everybody can afford a pet like Chocolate. There are many, many unhappy people out there. And at the same time, just as many unhappy dogs, abused, abandoned, waiting for adoption hopelessly...."

That's why you're not as happy as I am, Mimi. We never have these sudden qualms!

"What's that got to do with Chocolate?" Aba retorts. "You sound like Judas in *Jesus Christ Superstar*. So let me quote JC's reply. 'There will be poor always, pathetically struggling. Look at the good things you've got'!"

He used to sing that as my lullaby – starting with "Sleep and I shall soothe you".

"I just want to make sure we're doing the right thing." Mimi is talking at cross-purposes with Aba. "You pamper me, you always do, like when I go on wild shopping sprees.... I want you to tell me when I'm doing something wrong, for a change."

I wouldn't want that, no thanks. I know when I've done something wrong, such as waiting for my walk too long and wetting the carpet under the grand piano. Then I hide under the table or the piano with my very transparent guilty look, awaiting the pleasure of Mimi the Judge Supremo.

"No, you and I are doing the right thing for sure!" Aba is practically lecturing now. "Remember that columnist's piece on dogs I showed you? Saying dogs by nature know how to fill their relatively short life with happiness, that man has just failed to grasp that feat throughout the centuries, and wastes decades in his lifespan unhappily, looking for happiness. Chocolate brings happiness to us. That's his purpose in this world. We are blessed to have Chocolate!"

And I am blessed to have such a family too!

"You just keep saying that…."

"But that's the truth! Remember how we were, our family, before Chocolate arrived? Phoebe couldn't adapt to Hong Kong after spending ten years in England, and our formerly most cheerful daughter left us again, sourly, for Australia. Phoebus came home sulking every night after a terrible day at work. Fabian wouldn't even talk to us when he was a teenager here, and then he left for England too and then the States ... and these two old fools as you call us were left alone, our love long gone cold and stale like leftovers left out overnight…."

Well, those often got reheated in the middle of the night by Phoebus to fill him up before he hit the sack!

"And then…?" from Mimi, testingly.

And then I came.

"And then Seth came." Aba surprises us, at least me. "We had a fresh breeze penetrating the stagnant air we were in. Then Seth went, and I saw you in the same state as when Phoebe had just gone to England when she was thirteen. You were pining and weeping and lying sick in bed for months, until she returned on a home visit during the first term break."

I've heard about that, and about how Lena spilled the beans to Phoebe during that home visit, that Aba had been watching videos of Phoebe's piano performances every night too, wiping his eyes secretly.

"But Seth's gone for good now," responds Mimi, almost sobbing.

"Well," Aba goes on, "Marsha did to him what we did to Phoebe. It's for their own good that we let them leave for greener pastures abroad."

Well, don't worry about me. I can go to greener pastures

in my dream. No need to send me anywhere.

"And the point is…?" Mimi asks.

The point is you two did the right thing sacrificing yourselves for your child's welfare.

"The point is," Aba puts it more comprehensively, "We suffer loneliness and separation from our little princess yet again for a worthy cause – her happiness!"

Yeah, and Marsha did that to Seth too.

"Alright, that's Phoebe's bit. Let's get back to Chocolate's. So who's making whom happy? You make me so confused." Mimi just won't be satisfied. "Are we making Chocolate happy or the other way round? And which is the right thing? The right way?"

"Silly girl!" Before I can sort out Mimi's jumbled questions, Aba has got a ready answer, "Who's making who happy between the two of us? You follow?"

I see what you mean, Aba.

"I follow," nods Mimi. "Love is doing our best to make each other happy. – That's your worn-out cliché repeated umpteen times since time immemorial."

Is it? But I'm only hearing it now for the first time. And Mimi, aren't "umpteen times" and "time immemorial" worn out clichés too?

"Be honest with yourself," Aba goes on. "You take Chocolate to the Peak, to Dogs' Park, to Park Island…to all those places where he can have fun. How do you feel when you see he's having a good time?"

Yes, how? I'd like to know too. I know I was having a good time and I'm grateful for that. But were you sharing my joy too?

"Why, just like old times! How did we feel when we took Phoebe to the playground, or Phoebus to Ocean Park, took the whole family to Japan or Thailand?"

Oh, no! Don't give that sort of example. I was most miserable when you people had your trips abroad during summer holidays! I slept in your empty bed and longed for your return....

"And there's something in common between, say, Chocolate and Phoebus that I've noticed." Aba mercifully changes the subject.

Yes, our sharp ears, right? Quicker than our eyes – he's myopic and I've got overgrown hair blocking my eyes, more often than not.

"What's that?" Mimi asks.

"When Phoebus started playing the piano in the mall on weekends," Aba soliloquizes, "I must admit at first I was not too amused. I wished he would take up a proper, decent and respectable job like teaching music at a school or be a concert pianist playing only classical music."

He didn't want that, Aba. That wouldn't suit Phoebus at all.

"But he just wouldn't do that," Mimi concurs with me.

"No," Aba continues. "And the realization came to me that Mother's Day when we visited the mall to watch his performance and he dedicated a song to you, John Denver's *Perhaps Love*. And there were all those fans of his there. Young girls mostly. But also boys with camcorders who took video recordings. And housewives from the New Territories came out here every weekend just to hear him play. And there was a young couple who were both obese and apparently always looked down upon. Remember what they said to us? 'Your son is doing something great. He's bringing happiness to so many of us who've been hard-pressed for the whole week, and then on weekends we come to listen to him and watch him play and we feel so relaxed and refreshed. There's even this boy who went on stage to sing a love song to his girl-friend, with Phoebus accompanying him, and then proposed to her in public, and got himself engaged on the very spot...' You remember that?"

"Yes, I do."

No, I don't. But you are telling me. So what's your point?

"My point is," Aba explains himself. "Only then did I realize that Phoebus was doing something perhaps more meaningful than being a music teacher or concert pianist. He's bringing happiness to a considerable number of mall shoppers who may not ordinarily have the chance to get in touch with live music performance. And it is since then that I've revised my snobbish musical taste. I now say so openly, on the radio programme I host, that music in my view should not be rigidly divided into classical and pop. There is only good music and bad music to one's ears, and to each his own taste. That's why, on top of my Sunday Opera programme on Radio 4, I also did that series on Broadway and West End musicals on Radio 2...."

Hey, Aba, you've lost me before you're half way through that long-winded soliloquy. How can you expect to hold my attention span for so long? I am giving up this three-way dialogue – or is it trialogue? – that we are having, since you and Mimi can't hear me anyway, even though I am thinking aloud.

Instead I turn to see how Mr Zang is feeling about this couple staying at their table long after signing the tab. Here he comes, bringing the thermos and feigning thoughtfulness in refilling their teapot.

"Let's go," Mimi stands up abruptly. "And let's talk as we walk."

She takes up the bag hurriedly, amidst Mr Zang's goodbye greetings, "Thank you, come again...."

"But," Aba follows her clumsily and, as we stand on the escalator, hastens to enquire, "Did you follow my reasoning?"

"Loud and clear, Sir," answers Mimi with a sweet smile. "Point number one, Chocolate comes to us as an angel of happiness, same as Phoebe first did. Point number two,

Phoebus brings happiness to a lot of people by playing at the mall."

And what's that to me? I can't help asking, as Mimi unzips the bag at the top of the escalator, Aba pushes the glass door open, and they step out into the night street.

"Point number three," Aba takes over, "Chocolate brings happiness to our family in a similar way as Phoebus does to his fans. We see him having a good time and we all share his cheerfulness."

"Chocolate's purpose in life is therefore..." Mimi begins.

"Making himself happy," Aba finishes, "and through that, making everybody around him happy too!"

Now I follow you two! And by now we have reached the parked car.

"We love you, Chocolate," Mimi gives me a kiss on the tip of my brown nose as she opens the car door. As an expert flatterer, I reciprocate with an exceptionally watery slurp on her cheek.

"Just don't leave him alone in the car when you go to buy bread or whatever, or he will step on that button again, set off the burglar alarm, and attract an audience!"

Aba is a spoilsport! You have to bring that up at such a heart-warming moment?

"But," a sudden idea occurs to Mimi, "if Chocolate can bring happiness to all the people around him, why confine it to our family?"

"Right," once again Aba has the ready answer. "Enrol him as a Pet Doctor then!"

That reminds me of my first visit to the vet for shots against rabies and the rest of the lot.

While waiting at the vet's at that time, Mimi chatted with another more seasoned dog-owner, who told her about the Pet Doctor scheme, which first trains dogs and then takes them to visit old peoples' homes and hospitals to bring happiness to the old, the poor and the sick.

Mimi was so impressed that, at the end of that visit, she asked the nurse at the veterinary clinic, "How does one get to be a Pet Doctor?"

Mistaking her question as being how does one become a veterinary surgeon, the nurse replied, "Well, one must go and study at an overseas university...."

The nurse never understood why Mimi gave her that strange look as she hurried off with me.

But back to the present. As Mimi starts the car and pulls out, Aba asks, "You understand my points so readily.... No, you've never been this quick on the uptake, so this can only mean one thing. – You knew what I was going to say. – In that case, why did you ask when you already knew the answer?"

"So I can hear you say it once again, silly." Mimi gives him that sweet smile again. "Just as I ask you, do you still love me, am I still attractive, that sort of thing. Women do that."

Cosi fan tutte!

Well, Mimi, that's one blessing you and I share in common.

Our secret formula for happiness.

We never tire of doing the same enjoyable things over and over again!

With that comforting thought, I nestle beside Mimi who's driving us home, on Aba's lap, enjoying the massage of his affectionately caressing hand.

Smug and snug.

.

10. Epilogue – *Médecin Sans Souper*

There was only silence, and stillness, all wrapped up in total darkness.

Then there was light – a bright sun shining above. A boundless green lawn bestrewn with flowers of every colour of the rainbow....

Somehow I have got this nagging feeling of *déjà vu*.... Yes, I've been here before. I've seen this before.

Suddenly, without warning, some projectile flew overhead.

It stopped, hanging in mid air, just above my head.

I could therefore make out clearly what it was: a multi-coloured juicy piece of lamb shank, dripping blood, oozing fat, emitting a tempting aroma....

And then it all vanished abruptly!

Snapping out of it, I am back in the present. (I've definitely experienced the same thing before.)

I open my eyes which have been shut. So all that vista has been a dream.

And I realize why I had such a dream.

I am starving!

And I am shut up in the dark of the bag. Deposited – I insist on using that word and not, "put down" – having heard about the fate of too many strays – under Mimi's chair, in a restaurant. They are having dinner. I can tell by my nose this is a Japanese restaurant. They are having sushi: Californian, with crab roe and avocado.

It is the evening of the Dragon Boat Festival: a feast day commemorating a loyal patriot two millennia ago who leaped into the river and drowned himself. (His state had fallen to the army of the first Emperor of Qin, and he presciently understood that the Qin Emperor's desire to unify China was the ambition of a tyrant.) Hence, every year on this anniversary of his death, dragon-boat races are held, with a drummer at the bow of each dragon-boat and two rows of oarsmen paddling to the drumbeat, and glutinous rice dumplings wrapped in lotus leaves thrown into the water. The former are to scare off, and the latter to feed all the underwater creatures, so they wo'n't molest the patriot's drowned body. This tradition has been kept throughout the centuries, and today it is a public holiday.

Talking, I mean musing about dumplings, my recollection goes back to this morning and my breakfast.

At first I was not sure if this was a weekday or weekend. Last Sunday seemed less than a week ago, but Lena was off this morning, although – as usual on her off days – she took me downstairs for my morning walk and gave me breakfast before dressing prettily and going out. Also I was given my weekend breakfast of lamb shank!

That was the only meal I've had today.

Aba also went for his morning walk at the later, weekend hour, as opposed to the earlier weekday hour. On his return Mimi was still there. So this was a holiday, I concluded. And they both stared at me with a queer look when I showed excitement at that discovery.

"Do you think he will do well at the test this afternoon?" Mimi asked.

"I have full confidence in our good boy," Aba replied. "He'll pass with flying colours."

"I sincerely hope so." Mimi turned to me, "Hello, Dr Chocolate to be!"

At that point I remembered what was happening today. I was to attend the qualifying test for becoming a Doctor Pet.

"Well," Aba pondered, "when I was a student, my father hoped I'd read medicine. He was very disappointed when I switched to the arts stream in sixth form. And none of my three children chose medical studies either. Now, at last, our last-born boy may yet become a doctor!"

Then they went on to discuss the programme for the day.

The test would be in the late afternoon. Lena had given me a bath yesterday and I was brushed all spick-and-span this morning. So the usual holiday frolicking up on the Peak was out of the question.

"I don't want him all hyperactive and wild." Mimi shook her head. "Nor dishevelled and dirty either."

"But he should be kept in good spirits," argued Aba. "So let's take him to play a bit, mildly, at Dogs' Park."

Then we, Aba and I, spent the rest of the morning waiting for Mimi to get ready.

She had to make up and dress well, remember? And she kept receiving phone calls that further delayed that already long process. It usually allows Aba to finish watching a full-length movie on Cable TV. This morning he finished two.

By that time, Phoebus and Fabian had got up as well.

Just in time to hear Mimi announce, after hanging up, that Auntie Apple and Uncle Patrick had asked them all to lunch, to farewell Fabian who would shortly be posted to Singapore by his Bank.

There goes my Dogs' Park romp! I was exasperated.

When we finally set off, Aba and I were both sullen.

When Mimi asked what the matter was, Aba acted as my spokesman. "We said we were going to Dogs' Park. Now Chocolate will be very disappointed. We said we wanted to let him have some fun and be relaxed and in good cheer before sitting the test. Now he will be morose and moody."

"Never mind," Mimi comforted him. But I remained unconsoled. "We can still play in Dogs' Park, or at EMax, after the test."

They had dim sum lunch in Central District. I was shut up in the bag between Mimi's and Aba's chairs. Most boring ordeal! Dim sum lunches last for an eternity!

When he studied in Grade 11 in Vancouver, Phoebus lodged with Apple whose family was living out their residence requirement there, so he is on very intimate terms with Auntie Apple and Uncle Patrick. Fabian vies with his elder brother as their favourite nephew. He used to be close to Ding Ding, Apple's youngest daughter of his same age. They served together at many a wedding, he in tuxedo and she in long gown, holding the ring and posy respectively and leading the procession into the church. Fabian took the standard primary school composition assignment on "What I want to be when I grow up" very seriously. He changed his mind several times between doctor, lawyer and fireman, and consulted widely among family members. Once he asked Mimi, "Is a Catholic priest a respectable occupation?"

Mimi cautiously said yes, very much looked up to, but qualified that priests could not get married.

"Oh, then it's not for me," said Fabian, remembering his happy experience at weddings, "I love getting married! I enjoy it very much every time." He was six years old then. He thought he was getting married at every wedding he served as a bridal page!

Uncle Patrick and Auntie Apple gave Fabian best wishes and some helpful advice. Patrick promised to look him up on his next business trip to Singapore. They then gave Phoebus in turn some *uncleanly* – that's what I supposed "uncle-an'-auntie-ly" – meant counselling….

I fell asleep, hypnotized by the lecture.

And I had my panoramic multi-coloured dream again. This time I dreamed I was dressed in a white gown, with a stethoscope hanging on my chest. A name tag on my breast-pocket read "Dr Chocolate". A projectile flew overhead. It was a sick cat – as sick as a cat could be….

I woke up when the bag was lifted. Lunch was over. Having bade Uncle and Auntie goodbye, Phoebus proposed, "Let's get Chocolate out for a walk."

"No," vetoed Mimi. "We go straight to take a taxi home. No time."

They kept me in the bag for taxi rides, not to save the surcharge for bringing pets, but to save me from the discriminatory attitudes of most taxi drivers against animals.

I didn't quite follow their reasoning. Roughly it was something like this: they took a taxi to Central so they didn't have to spend time parking the car and be late for the lunch appointment. And then they hastened home again to get the car and drive to EMax, where I would take the test at 1600 hours, to ensure I am on time.

So which has a higher risk of being late, driving or not driving?

Fabian left on his own to watch the Dragon Boat race at Stanley, since his Bank had entered a team in this contest. I got the feeling of *déjà vu* again when he told his parents, "They asked me to be the drummer. I turned them down."

Mimi and Aba intended to take me to the test together, and Phoebus also volunteered to join in to cheer me up.

I was let out of the bag, once inside the family car.

Mimi was driving. Aba was sitting next to her and navigating, i.e. giving her detailed instructions on each turn to take. Mimi had monopolized the driver's seat from time immemorial. She was the better driver and had better eyesight. But Aba knew all the routes and places. So Mimi described the two of them as "the blind and the crippled". It was a fable she told her students, about a blind man carrying a cripple on his back and escaping from being trapped in a house on fire, the blind man relying on the cripple's directions on where to go, and the cripple having the blind man as his legs. A complementary duo, that's the moral.

Sitting with me in the back seat, Phoebus started asking Mimi what Doctor Pet was all about.

"Dogs who qualify as Doctor Pets – or is it Doctor's Pet? – will be voluntary workers teamed up with their humans, "good-deed-doers," as the Wizard of Oz puts it. They will go on visiting assignments, at hospitals, homes for the aged, orphanages, sheltered workshops, special education centres for the retarded, the autistic and the like, to bring love, care, comfort and joy to the underprivileged," Mimi replied.

"Where did you read all that stuff?" Phoebus asked again.

"I've been reading the book by Ms Luk the founder and head of Doctor Pet, called *Happiness is right beside you*, telling stories about ten dogs, all Doctor Pets. Aba bought it for my bedtime reading."

"Well," Phoebus commented, "Sounds a very worthy cause. And Chocolate will surely make a good Doctor Pet. Why, he brings happiness to our whole family. He will bring it to everybody he visits too."

Well, can't say I'm not quite justly proud of myself. I've heard Mimi and Aba sing my praises so often. They explain, for instance, to many people why they chose a toy poodle. For its three distinct and invaluable attributes: it does not shed hair, it does not smell, and it does not bark – at least no irritating, compulsive and prolonged barking fits like many other small dogs with feelings of insecurity.

And I remember the Pets Benediction Sunday at the Cathedral – the Cathedral of the Immaculate Conception – where the bishop is based. Mimi took me there to receive the Vicar General's blessing, along with hundreds of other pets, from hamsters, birds and turtles to cats and dogs. These pets were paraded one by one before the gathering in the outdoor car-park in front of the Cathedral. And when it was Mimi's turn to introduce me, she spoke into the microphone, "Chocolate is a great cohesive force in our family. We all feel happier and more intimately knit together since he came into the family." But when she tried to make me display my feat of jumping through the hoop of her arms, I was distracted by the hubbub around me and did not readily comply. The Vicar General, unwilling to delay the procession, said, "Let him do it some other time," and proceeded to make the sign of the cross and sprinkle holy water on my head. (So the one time I failed Mimi I was absolved immediately.) I guess since then I have truly become a puppy full of God's grace!

Carried away by these reminiscences, I was unaware of being taken upstairs at EMax, after alighting in the car-park, to the pet shop floor labelled Pet Max. But I immediately recognized my favourite indoor haunt and dashed right into the best-smelling shop: a shop selling cat food! It seems that cats don't have to perform tricks but still eat better than us. No wonder so many people say cats are smarter than dogs.

They dragged me out from the cat-food shop and took me to the counter of the test venue to register. Aba filled in the forms neatly and efficiently for Mimi and himself as owners, pausing only over the "age" item and asked Mimi which box to tick for her.

With one look at Aba that made him cower, Mimi pointed to the left-hand box saying "Twenty-six to fifty-nine".

"This one, of course!"

The right-hand box was "Sixty and over".

Yes, Aba was indeed foolish to ask!

Having handed in the form, we were asked to wait outside the interviewing room. I remembered its glass doors, inside which we had witnessed obedience classes taking place on previous visits. Now they were covered up by Doctor Pet posters so one could not see what was going on inside.

I chatted with the Bernese mountain dog (he had the border collie's face and the St Bernard's size) and another toy poodle (apricot colour) waiting in the queue. Essentially our conversation was that of gourmets comparing notes on a floor where the shelves are filled with dog food.

Meanwhile Phoebus called Danielle his girlfriend who had just gone off duty, asking her to join us. Poor Danielle, having to work on a holiday, and plainly missing me...oh, and Phoebus too, perhaps.

Then Phoebus shivered involuntarily and said to Mimi and Aba, "I feel more nervous now, waiting with Chocolate, even more nervous than waiting to play at my own piano competition when I was small!"

That would be something!

I remember hearing them relate how Phoebus lost that competition, having made too many mistakes due to nervousness. Aba's face was all clouded over. And the adjudicator from England noticed it and came over and tried to console him, almost apologetic for giving Phoebus a low score.

"Your son is very talented. It does not really matter too much whether he wins or loses. I'm quite positive he's meant for higher things...."

"He shouldn't have made those mistakes. He could have played that piece so much better." That was Aba's reaction, "He let me down!"

And Mimi went on to tell how Aba was so upset he walked round and round in the neighbourhood of the competition venue to let off steam before he could go back to work.

Recalling all that made me a bit nervous too. It was a very awkward moment of suspense, waiting for my turn to face my trial! Mimi, Aba and Phoebus were all on edge and at a loss what to do. They did not dare play with me lest I got too excited, nor make me rehearse my tricks lest I got fed up....

Then, my turn came.

I was literally snatched from Mimi, who was told to stay outside the room and wait to be called, and bundled into the test room, the glass doors closing behind me.

It was a very spacious and cavernous room. Chairs lined the wall on one side. On the opposite side two ladies sat at a table with their backs to the wall. Obviously the examiners. And against the innermost wall, a blue cloth backdrop hung over a chair or stool, more like a covered pedestal, hidden under the cloth. Studio lighting was set up there, complete with white umbrellas. A man who seemed to be the photographer, with a large professional-looking camera hanging on his chest, was standing by, with a Schnauzer dressed in a skirt by his side.

Remembering my manners, I first approached the two ladies and gave them friendly greetings: wagging my tail and scratching their knees with my fore paws. They responded with amiable smiles.

Next I approached the Schnauzer.

"Hi, I'm Chocolate. How are you?"

"I'm Bo Bo, ahem." She put on airs. "DOCTOR Bo Bo, if you please!"

"Wow," I put on an appearance of being impressed. "You must be most talented!" My silly boyish grin came in handy.

"Well, I know a trick or two...."

By this time we were so familiar we started wrestling, which meant we stood on our hind legs and grappled with each other with our fore legs. Actually a mix between waltzing and sumo.

Just before I got totally carried away, Mimi and Aba were ushered into the chamber. Bo Bo leaped away from me at once, resuming her proud air and walking back to the studio set-up.

My parents sat down on those chairs against the far wall, facing the interviewers at the table against the opposite wall, and putting on very solemn and stiff expressions.

I did what a last-born child was expected to do on seeing his parents. I bounced with joy and whined and whimpered, pawing Mimi who seemed embarrassed with my behaviour.

"Sit. Stay," she commanded and I at once obeyed. Sitting on my haunches in the middle of the room, equidistant from interviewers and interviewees. Quiet and still.

After some polite overture, one interviewer, Bo Bo's human I gathered, started asking questions.

"Where did you learn about Doctor Pet?"

"From friends and pamphlets." answered Mimi.

Mimi, you should mention the book you read. There's the author sitting there, the other so far silent interviewer! I recognized her face as the same as the one on the back cover of the book on your bedside table.

"Why do you want to join this Scheme?" the questioning continued.

"I'm a school teacher and I have experience with children. I pay special attention to those with family or personal problems like belonging to a single-parent household, suffering from autism and so forth. I think I can use my experience to help your worthy cause."

"Just what exactly do you think you can contribute to this Scheme?"

Isn't that asking the same question over again in a different way?

"I am retiring soon. So I'll have plenty of time. I think I can contribute a lot."

Mimi, you should mention ME! And my special talents. All that bringing happiness to the underprivileged stuff! Not just talking about yourself. But it's too late now….

"And what can he" – the grand inquisitor consulted the form – "Chocolate, what can he do? Can you give a demonstration, please?"

"Certainly." At this point Mimi came up to me and rehearsed with me the whole routine, "Sit. Gimme five. Next hand. High ten. Swing. Jump. Jump. Jump…."

And at my fourth leap through her hands' hoop, the

examiner interrupted, before I could go on to do roll over and play dead.

"That will do. Thank you," and at once she looked down at the papers on her table. "We'll let you know within a month."

And all the while, Aba was mute and grinning like a silly boy. For once we were look-alikes.

"Now please go over there to pose for a couple of pictures." – The interviewer pointed to the salon set-up and blue backdrop.

Mimi placed me on the pedestal – a very apt metaphor which our real life acted out – covered by the blue backdrop, where I exhibited my usual fashion-model pose for my solo shot taken by the photographer. Then Mimi sat down in my place, holding me in her arms with my hind legs standing on her lap, her arm around my chest and my fore legs resting on her arm, my whole belly and private parts exposed – most indecorous!

"Heads closer together please," said the cameraman and we went cheek to cheek before he took the duet shot.

Then we were dismissed. Only then did Mimi accost the silent second interviewer.

"I've read your book, Ms Luk. Very touching!"

"Oh, thank you." She answered, embarrassed.

And that's it. Test over. We came out of the glass doors. Bo Bo sneaked out too, escaping from the ennui of being assistant examiner of inter-dog relations all day long! Somebody went after her, calling her name.

Danielle had arrived by this time. Mimi described briefly what the test entailed. The mystery to them all was what I did, or what was done to me – or as they collectively chanted at mass, "What I have done and what I have failed to do" – when I was in that room on my own before Mimi and Aba were admitted!

By then I was very hungry. I therefore distinctly

remembered Mimi's promise while we were waiting for my turn to be tested.

"Chocolate, do your level best! After the test I'll treat you to a real big feast!"

Well, she was so excited, narrating the story to Phoebus and Danielle, she seemed to have clean forgotten her pledge. So I wandered around the Pet Max floor, sniffing and salivating in front of many a shelf of dog food galore.

Instead of honouring her word, Mimi offered me a game of fetch, or catch, throwing the rubber ball for me to chase after.

"Now you can have some fun," as if she was doing me a great favour.

But I didn't want to play, I wanted to be fed!

Involuntarily I went after the ball, but only half-heartedly.

After what seemed to me long, long last, we left in the car. Mimi dropped Phoebus and Danielle off at Happy Valley – Danielle's parents were meeting Phoebus's family in the coming week and the youngsters were booking a table at the restaurant where the New China News Agency used to be (so they would go there again after all, but without me!) – and drove home.

Good, home meant feeding me at long last! But on the way they made phone calls. One to a department store, ascertaining its opening hours. The other to Fabian at home, back from the Dragon Boat regatta.

"You want to shop for travelling bags? The emporium closes at seven. So come downstairs and wait for us to pick you up."

And so, the car stopped only for a second at our building to pick up Fabian, at 6:30 pm, then drove straight on to town. Mimi parked in the department store car-park, put me in the bag but only half zipped it so my head could stick out. And we all went shopping in the luggage department.

And sure enough, the mission completed before seven, with Fabian having quickly but successfully chosen two bags, one large and one small, for his imminent trip to Singapore. In that half-hour I managed to bewitch all the salesladies and shoppers who saw me. Even though I put on my grumpy look because I was in a department selling something I hated most!

"Now let's grab a bite!" Mimi proposed.

I second the motion most heartily!

That completes my total recall on Dragon Boat Festival, 2009.

They drove straight to this Japanese Restaurant, and were soon rejoined by Phoebus and Danielle too.

At this point I emerge from my reminiscences and enter fully into the present moment, with the burning sensation of acute hunger....

"Being a Doctor Pet calls for sacrifice," Mimi is saying, "And I am ready for it! And so are you, Doctor Chocolate!"

That's easy for you to say. Am I supposed to sacrifice by starving to death just to be Doctor Chocolate?

Please, Mimi, for mercy's sake, don't place too heavy a burden on my shoulders. I am, after all, "only a dog" – as you put it when you were coming out of the Shanghai Memories Restaurant.

And that, as Samuel Johnson entitled his last chapter in *Rasselas*, is "The Conclusion in which Nothing is Concluded"!

Quoth Chocolate, Doctor-designate, *médicin sans souper*.

June 2009

Characters in the Story

FAMILY

Aba Papa in the Family who served as scribe in chronicling Chocolate's autobiography. Full-time administrator at the University of Hong Kong (HKU) and freelance jack-of-all-trades (but master of none).

Chocolate Australian-born toy poodle brought into The Family as last-born child, who dictated his autobiography (Part 1: My First 33 Months) through transmission of brainwaves.

Danielle At the time of writing, girlfriend of Phoebus (now Phoebus' wife). Fellow Chinese University of Hong Kong (CUHK) graduate. Plays the flute. Resident in Hong Kong.

Fabian Third- (and would be last- if it were not for Chocolate) born son. Graduate of University of Michigan, Ann Arbor, USA. Resident in Singapore.

Lena Domestic helper from the Philippines who has served in the Family since Fabian was two years old and has long been considered a member of the Family.

Mimi Aba's wife, Chocolate's Mama, and undisputed Head of the Family. Teacher at a primary school.

Phoebe First-born daughter of the Family now resident in Sydney, Australia. Graduate of London School of Economics (LSE).

Phoebus Second-born son. Won soubriquet of "Piano Prince". Graduate in music of The Chinese University of Hong Kong (CUHK). Resident in Hong Kong.

RELATIVES

Apple and Patrick Sister of Mimi and her husband, humans of Bobby and Happy, parents to Ding Ding (their youngest of three daughters) who used to serve with Fabian as bridal flower-girl and page respectively.

Bobby Bichon frise cousin of Chocolate, a boy.

Cosy Yorkshire terrier cousin of Chocolate, a female.

Happy	Bichon frise cousin of Chocolate, a girl.
Roger and Emily	Brother and sister-in-law of Aba, humans of Snoopy.
Snoopy	Husky cousin of Chocolate, a boy.
Veronica	Sister of Mimi, human of Cosy. (Her husband Michael and daughter Esther are not mentioned in the book.)

FRIENDS

Bean Bean	Greedy and shrewd food-hunter friend of Chocolate, co-third in obstacle race at Dogs' Park with Chocolate when Bobby was first runner up.
Bo Bo	Pet doctor kept by Ms Luk; on the interviewing team for pet-doctor applicants on the day Chocolate attended. Ms Luk is the author of the Chinese book, "Happiness is right beside you".
Cardos	White Labrador retriever neighbour of Chocolate (who has since ascended to canine heaven).
Emily	Golden retriever neighbour.
Esteban	Bull terrier neighbour.
Ice and Cream	Toy poodles of the owner/photographer of Dog Paradise (which has now ceased business).
Lucky Mui	A girl Shih Tzu of unconfirmed age, adopted by Rufina. Chocolate's partner at Valentine's Day dinner in 2009. ("Mui" means "Lass".)
Marsha	Original human of Seth. Singer/model/dancer/film actress.
Mr Zang	Maitre d' at Shanghai Memories Restaurant.
Pei Pei	Marsha's mother, veteran film actress in Hong Kong. She played the part of the villain who kills with poisoned darts the hero – played by Chow Yun Fat – in the film "Crouching Tiger and Hidden Dragon" by Lee Ang. Her other daughter in the USA now takes care of Seth.
Rufina	Goddaughter of Mimi, human of Lucky Mui.
Rumble	Bull-dog neighbour bullied by Chocolate.
Seth	Red toy poodle, now emigrated to Los Angeles, USA.
The Chais	Not mentioned by name. The husband is a Hong

	Kong Government official responsible for converting the Wanchai Waterfront Promenade into a temporary Dogs' Park (now closed); a fellow Riccian of Aba's. (That is, he and Aba were fellow residents at Ricci Hall, a residential hostel at HKU run by Jesuits). His wife is a former classmate of Mimi's.
The ex-boyfriend	Pop singer and television artiste in Hong Kong who bought Seth as a gift to Marsha when she was his girlfriend.
The Fans	Fan Shu (Potato), Fan Gua (Pumpkin) and Fan Gung (At work), three toy poodles kept by Queenie the proprietor and serving as resident public relations officers of Dog Café. (The Dog Café has now changed hands and Queenie now spends all day taking good care of them.)
The third Riccian	Recalled by Aba as a fellow penniless Riccian in the dance hostess adventure, courtesy of Vincent's father; as "tall and handsome". Years later he gave a reunion party at his mansion for Aba and Vincent. He worked for Cathay Pacific Airways, then for Hong Kong Telecom/PCCW, and for a short while at Asia Television Hong Kong. At present he is Chairman of the Board, HKU School of Professional and Continuing Education (SPACE). Known as Linus to his friends.
Two Chow Chows	Kept by Vincent and Maggie and not yet met by Chocolate.
Two Huskies	Neighbours bullied by Chocolate (unchronicled) who used to live at Number 2, University Drive on the HKU campus when the Wills, their humans, were on the staff of HKU. (Barry Will was once Dean of Architecture: both the Wills have now retired and no longer live in HKU staff-quarters.)
Vincent and Maggi	Friends of Aba at HKU, Vincent being another fellow Riccian of Aba's.

Glossary and Notes

Abbellimenti	Ornaments.
CSI	Crime Scene Investigation. The acronym, "CSI", is the title of more than one American TV series on forensic science used in solving tough cases, including CSI Miami and CSI NYPD (New York Police Department). In Hong Kong, we might refer instead to police forensic procedures.
DNA	Deoxyribonucleic acid, a nucleic acid that contains the genetic instructions used in the development and functioning of all known living organisms.
GCSE	General Certificate of Secondary Education.
Grades	In the Canadian School System, Grade 1 to Grade 12 are equivalent in the Hong Kong School System to Primary 1 to the Upper Sixth Form. Grades 11 and 12 are the Canadian equivalent of Lower and Upper Sixth Forms in Hong Kong and the United Kingdom.
HD	High Definition [television].
HKU	The University of Hong Kong.
I-Bank	Investment Bank.
Presbyopia	The deterioration of eyesight with age, resulting in difficulty in reading small print and seeing clearly things close (under one's nose).
PTA	Parent Teacher Association, normally associated with a single school: bodies notoriously responsible for much extra stress for teachers in Hong Kong.
SAA	Society for Abandoned Animals.
SPCA	Society for the Prevention of Cruelty to Animals.
Undercroft	Term used on the University of Hong Kong estate for the covered (and cement-floored) part outside the lift lobby, separating the uncovered driveway on one side and the uncovered lawn on the other of the building (referring here specifically to Number 2, University Drive).

About Proverse Hong Kong

Proverse Hong Kong, co-founded by Gillian and Verner Bickley, is based in Hong Kong with strong regional and international connections.

Verner Bickley has led cultural and educational centres, departments, institutions and projects in many parts of the world. Gillian Bickley has recently concluded a career as a University teacher of English Literature spanning four continents. Proverse Hong Kong draws on their combined academic, administrative and teaching experience as well as varied long-term participation in reading, research, writing, editing, indexing, reviewing, publishing and authorship.

Proverse Hong Kong has published novels, novellas, non-fiction (including history, sport, travel), single-author poetry collections, young teens and academic books. Other interests include biography, memoirs and diaries, and academic works in the humanities, social sciences, cultural studies, linguistics and education. Some Proverse books have accompanying audio texts. Proverse works with texts by non-native-speaker writers of English as well as by native English-speaking writers.

Proverse welcomes authors who have a story to tell, a person they want to memorialize, a neglect they want to remedy, a record they want to correct, a strong interest that they want to share, information or perceptions they want to offer, skills they want to teach, and who consciously seek to make a contribution to society in an informative, interesting and well-written way.

The name, "Proverse", combines the words "prose" and "verse" and is pronounced accordingly.

THE PROVERSE PRIZE

The Proverse Prize, an annual international competition for an unpublished publishable book-length work of fiction, non-fiction, or poetry, was established in January 2008. It is open to all who are at least eighteen on the date they sign the entry form and without restriction of nationality, residence or citizenship.

Its objectives are: to encourage excellence and / or excellence and usefulness in publishable written work in the English Language, which can, in varying degrees, "delight and instruct". Entries are invited from anywhere in the world.

HONORARY ADVISORS (2009-)

Marion Bethel (poet, the Bahamas), David Crystal (linguist and lexicographer, United Kingdom), Björn Jernudd (linguist, Sweden), Larry Smith (cultural administrator, USA), Edwin Thumboo (poet and academic, Singapore), Olga Walló (novelist, translator, Czech Republic).

CO-FOUNDERS

Dr Verner Bickley, MBE and Dr Gillian Bickley.
~~To celebrate their lifelong love of words in any form, as readers, listeners, performers, teachers, academics, writers, editors, indexers and now publishers.

Summary Terms and Conditions (for indication only & subject to revision)

The information in this book is for guidance only. Please refer to the Entry Form & Terms & Conditions on the Proverse Hong Kong website: <http://www.proversepublishing.com>. Each forthcoming year's version will be uploaded before the closing date for entries each year. In the meantime, the previous year's version is available for guidance and reference.

The Prize
1) Publication by Proverse Hong Kong.
2) Cash prize of HKD10,000 (HKD7.80 = approx. US$1.00)

Supplementary publication grants may be made to selected other entrants for publication by Proverse Hong Kong.

Depending on the quality of the work in any year, the prize may be shared by at most two entrants or withheld, as recommended by the judges.

The entry fee is HKD200 OR GBP30.

Writers are eligible, who are at least eighteen on the date they sign their entry form(s) for The Proverse Prize. There is no nationality or residence restriction.

Each submitted work must be an unpublished publishable single-author work of non-fiction, fiction or poetry, the original work of the entrant, and submitted in the English language. Plays and school textbooks are ineligible.

Translated work: If the work entered is a translation from a language other than English, both the original work and the translation should be previously unpublished. This is not a translation prize. The submitted work will not be judged as a translation but as an original work.

Extent of the Manuscript: within the range of what is usual for the genre of the work submitted. However, it is advisable that novellas be in the range 35,000 to 50,000 words); other fiction (e.g. novels, short-story collections) and non-fiction (e.g. autobiographies, biographies, diaries, letters, memoirs, essay collections, etc.) should be in the range, 80,000 to 110,000 words. Poetry collections should be in the range, 8,000 to 30,000 words. Other word-counts and mixed-genre submissions are not ruled out.

Writers may choose, if they wish, to obtain the services of an **Editor** in presenting their work, and should acknowledge this help and the nature and extent of this help in the Entry Form.

KEY DATES FOR THE AWARD OF THE PROVERSE PRIZE IN ANY YEAR (subject to confirmation*)

Deadline for receipt of Entry Fees/ Entry Forms	31 May of the year of entry
Deadline for receipt of entered manuscripts	30 June of the year of entry
Announcement of long-list	August-September of the year of entry*
Announcement of short-list	October-December of the year of entry*
Announcement of winner/ max two winners (sharing the cash prize)	December of the year of entry to April of the year that follows the year of entry*
Cash Award Made	Within the period, beginning in November of the year that follows the year of entry*
Publication of winning work(s)	Within the period, beginning in November of the year that follows the year of entry*

For full & up-to-date details and Entry Form please visit the Proverse Hong Kong Proverse Publishing website: <www.proversepublishing.com>.

Enquiries by email to <info@proversepublishing.com>.

Alternatively, up to 1 May annually, you may **request a copy of the details and entry form,** by **writing to:** "The Proverse Prize, Proverse Hong Kong, P.O. Box 259, Tung Chung Post Office, Tung Chung, Lantau Island, NT, Hong Kong, SAR, China", enclosing a large (A4 OR A5 size) self-addressed envelope. For enquiries from Hong Kong, please affix a HKD4.40 postage stamp. For international entries, please enclose seven IRC coupons.

Books published by, or available through, Proverse Hong Kong

http://www.proversepublishing.com

*Indicates a title is already available from our Hong Kong based Distributor, The Chinese University Press of Hong Kong, The Chinese University of Hong Kong, Shatin, NT, Hong Kong, SAR, China. Email: cup@cuhk.edu.hk

*CHINA SUITE AND OTHER POEMS by Gillian Bickley, Hong Kong and the UK, November 2009. pbk. c. 136pp. w. 2 no. audio CDs. Preface by Elbert S. P. Lee. Recommendation by Karmel Schreyer. Supported by the Hong Kong Arts Development Council. ISBN-13: 978-988-17724-9-7
www.chineseupress.com/asp/e_Book_card.asp?BookID=2658&Lang=E
24Reader Ebook edition (2010) ISBN 978-988-19320-4-4
"The poems in *China Suite* are unpretentious, direct, and even raw, like gemstones freshly dug out of a quarry. The psychological boundaries drawn to separate cultures from cultures, clans from clans, and individual from individual are utterly destroyed." — Elbert S. P. Lee
"A collection refined by the sensitivity and spirit of a poet who observes with the wonder and clarity of someone who is at once an insider and outsider. In her works, we see that Bickley's poetry has the ability to provide both spontaneous, on-the-spot immediacy and lingering, contemplative power...." — Hilary Chan Tsz-Shan, *Asian Cha*, February 2010 (Issue 10).

*CHOCOLATE'S BROWN STUDY IN THE BAG by Rupert Kwan Yun Chan, Hong Kong and the UK, March 2011. pbk. c. 112pp. plus 16 colour pp. Proverse Prize Finalist (2009). ISBN: 978-988-19932-1-2
"Rupert Chan has a light, humorous touch. Delightful. Witty". — Proverse Prize Judges, 2009.

*THE COMPLETE COURT CASES OF MAGISTRATE FREDERICK STEWART AS REPORTED IN *THE CHINA MAIL*, JULY 1881 TO MARCH 1882. Hong Kong and the UK, 2008. CD. 761pp. inc. notes, index. Preface by The Hon. Mr Justice Bokhary PJ, Court of Final Appeal. Edited by Gillian Bickley. Indexed by Verner Bickley. Supported by the Council of the Lord Wilson Heritage Trust. ISBN-13: 978-988-17724-1-1.
"Together [these brief reports] do even more for the modern reader than put him in the armchair of someone who took the *China Mail* in Victorian Hong Kong—although that alone would be interesting enough. They provide him with a seat at the back of Mr Stewart's court, alive again and in session."— The Hon. Mr Justice Bokhary PJ.

CULTURAL RELATIONS IN THE GLOBAL COMMUNITY: PROBLEMS AND PROSPECTS, 1981. hbk. 255pp. Edited by Verner Bickley and Puthenparampil John Philip. ISBN-10: 81-7017-136-9; ISBN-13: 978-81-7017-136-2.

*THE DEVELOPMENT OF EDUCATION IN HONG KONG, 1841-1897: AS REVEALED BY THE EARLY EDUCATION REPORTS OF THE HONG KONG GOVERNMENT, 1848-1896, ed. Gillian Bickley. Hong Kong and the United Kingdom, 2002. hbk. 633pp., inc. bibliography, index. The only collected, corrected, annotated, introduced, published edition of important source materials, with brief biographies of four of the writers *and archival photographs*. Supported by the Council of the Lord Wilson Heritage Trust. ISBN-10: 962-85570-1-7; ISBN-13: 978-962-85570-1-1.
www.chineseupress.com/asp/e_Book_card.asp?BookID=1526&Lang=E
"An essential resource for those researching colonial education policy." —Norman Miners, University of Hong Kong, in, *The Journal of Imperial and Colonial History*.

FOOTFALLS ECHO IN THE MEMORY: A Life With The Colonial Education Service And The British Council In Asia, by Verner Bickley. London and New York, 2010. hbk. xviii+314pp. w. 20 b/w photographs. Forewords by Rt Hon the Lord Hunt of Wirral, MBE and Valerie Mitchell, OBE, Director-General, the English-Speaking Union of the Commonwealth. Supported by the Hong Kong Arts Development Council. ISBN: 978-1-84885-085-9.
Verner Bickley reviews his eventful life in a series of memory-filled footsteps. The memoirs of someone who has quietly experienced a very full life, continues to serve and continues to give through the telling of his story. — Valerie Pickard, HKADC Examiner
"A man's experience of a changing world." —Alice Tsay, *Asian Cha*, May 2010 (Issue 11).

*FOR THE RECORD AND OTHER POEMS OF HONG KONG, by Gillian Bickley. Hong Kong and the UK, 2003. pbk. 118pp. w. author's portrait. Sixty poems written during a residence of 30 years in Hong Kong. With a talk given to the English Society of the University of Hong Kong. With two CDs of all poems read by the author. Preface by Rosanna Wong. Supported by the Hong Kong Arts Development Council. ISBN-10: 962-85570-2-5; ISBN-13: 978-962-85570-2-8. Mobibook e-book edition (2009) ISBN 978-988-99668-9-8.
www.chineseupress.com/asp/e_Book_card.asp?BookID=1732&Lang=E
People, nature, city-scenes, thoughts, experiences, cultural performances.
"Thought-provoking and entertaining." — David Wilson, *Sunday Morning Post*, Hong Kong.

Chocolate's Brown Study in the Bag

*FORWARD TO BEIJING! A GUIDE TO THE SUMMER OLYMPICS, by Verner Bickley. Hong Kong and the UK, 29 February 2008. pbk. 260pp. w. 16 b/w photographs & author's portrait. Message by Timothy Fok. Preface by the Hon. Dr. Arnaldo de Oliveira Sales. With an essay, "A Big Idea" by Chris Wardlaw. ISBN-13: 978-988-99668-3-6. Mobibook e-book edition (2008): ISBN-13: 978-988-99668-7-4
www.chineseupress.com/asp/e_Book_card.asp?BookID=2318&Lang=E
"Explains for each Olympic Sport the rules, special terms & vocabulary. Lists impressive Olympiad achievements of the past. Contains fascinating insights into the history of the Games. Showcases the Beijing Olympics, the third Asian Summer Olympiad. Provides for visitors, & residents of Beijing & Hong Kong useful information, phrases, dialogues, quizzes and conversational openers."
"Comprehensive and scholarly. The idea is noble: encourage visitors to embrace the symbolic gesture of this third Asian summer Olympiad—international goodwill, cooperation and peace." — *Hong Kong Magazine.*
"Will appeal to the adult 'armchair enthusiast' seeking to get the most out of televised events. Appeals across age and gender, designed for longevity." — Vincent Heywood, *Chinese Cross Currents.*

*GIN'S TONIC: OCEAN VOYAGE, INNER JOURNEY, by Virginia MacRobert. Preface by Ed Vaughan. Hong Kong and the UK, 2010, pbk. 560pp., w. inc. index. Illustrations: colour photographs, author portrait. Story of a journey round the world. Supported by Hong Kong Arts Development Council. ISBN-13: 978-988-17724-3-5.
www.chineseupress.com/asp/e_Book_card.asp?BookID=2736&lang=E
Mobipocket Ebook (2010) ISBN 978-988-18905-7-3
"What fun it will be to sail around the world with Ginni MacRobert as you read and ask yourself, 'what would I do now?!' It's an honour to welcome you aboard this book and to know that you are about to discover pure courage." — Ed Vaughan
—"The book is soft and refreshing and tingles one's heart in such a way that your feelings go along with *Dai Long Wan*. A book to be read with profit." — Stephen Tang (Gu Song).

*THE GOLDEN NEEDLE: THE BIOGRAPHY OF FREDERICK STEWART (1836-1889), by Gillian Bickley, David C. Lam Institute for East-West Studies, Hong Kong Baptist University. Hong Kong and the UK, 1997. pbk. 308pp., inc. bibliography, index. w. archival photographs. Foreword by Lady Saltoun. Introduction by Sir David Wilson (now Lord Wilson) ISBN-10: 962-80270-8-5; ISBN-13: 978-962-8027-08-8. Mobibook e-book edition. ISBN: 978-962-85570-6-6.
www.chineseupress.com/asp/e_Book_card.asp?BookID=1550&Lang=E
The biography of the Founder of Hong Kong Government Education and first headmaster of Queen's College (then the Central School).
"Dr Bickley's life of Frederick Stewart is beautifully written, eminently readable, and at times moving." — Lady Saltoun.
"We need more studies of this type to understand fully the complexities of colonial rule." "[I] thoroughly enjoyed this book." — Clive Whitehead, University of Western Australia, *Int. J. of Lifelong Education.*
"Bickley tells the story with unswerving admiration and many vivid touches." — Douglas Hurd, *The Scotsman.*

*THE GOLDEN NEEDLE: THE BIOGRAPHY OF FREDERICK STEWART (1836-1889). Full audio version on 14 CDs. Read by Verner Bickley. ISRC HK-D94-00-00001-40.
www.chineseupress.com/asp/e_Book_card.asp?BookID=1552&Lang=E

Also, TEACHERS' AND STUDENTS' GUIDE TO THE BOOK AND AUDIO BOOK OF 'THE GOLDEN NEEDLE: THE BIOGRAPHY OF FREDERICK STEWART (1836-1889)': Proverse Hong Kong Study Guides. Mobipocket e-book. ISBN-10: 962-85570-9-2; ISBN-13: 978-962-85570-9-7.
24Reader Ebook edition (2010) ISBN 978-988-19320-5-1

*HEART TO HEART, by Patty Ho. Hong Kong and UK. pbk. 104pp. Several 4C illustrations, reproductions of original artwork by the writer's sister, March 2010. Preface by Winston Ka-Sun Chu. Supported by the Hong Kong Arts Development Council. ISBN 978-988-17724-0-4
www.chineseupress.com/asp/e_Book_card.asp?BookID=2738&lang=E
24Reader Ebook edition (2010) ISBN 978-988-19320-6-8
"A remarkably engaging and edifying book of simple but thought-provoking poems, [a] timely reminder to the reading public that Hong Kong has more to offer than the sum of its literary, cultural and political stereotypes. If the concept of 'one world' is worth anything in this postmodern age of globalist cynicism, Patty Ho's poetry causes us to reflect on what is quintessentially human and on the fragile beauty of all existence." — Mike Ingham
— "Along with the carefully chosen photographs and thought-provoking watercolour illustrations provided by Ho's sister, the collection constitutes a dynamic conversation between visual and written texts about the emotions and values we all share."— Flora Mak, in *Cha: An Asian literary Journal*, Issue 12, September 2010.

*IMMORTELLE AND BHANDAARAA POEMS by Lelawattee Manoo-Rahming. Preface by Sandra Pouchet Paquet, PhD, Professor Emerita of English, University of Miami. Hong Kong and the UK, 9 March 2011. pbk.

Chocolate's Brown Study in the Bag

176pp. (plus 8 colour pp. w. 9 original pieces of artwork by the author.) Proverse Prize Finalist (2009). ISBN 978-988-19321-3-6.

Inspired by the Hindu philosophy of reincarnation, many of the poems are written in memory of loved ones, filled with scenes from the poet's physical landscape which spans the Caribbean, from The Bahamas, her present home, to Trinidad, the land of her birth. The language of these sensual poems is a syncretism of the poet's East Indian-derived Bhojpuri Hindi and her Trinbagonian creole, peppered with nuances of the Bahamian vernacular. This syncretism is reflected in the themes of the poems. Although many of the poems deal with Indo-Caribbean anthropology, the collection embraces other cultures and religions which are present in the Caribbean, and speaks to the fluidity in philosophy that can exist and flourish, in such plural societies.

Immortelle and Bhandaaraa Poems is a celebration of life and a testament to the lives of those who have passed on.

"Lelawattee Manoo-Rahming is a poet and mixed media artist of great range and complexity; all of the world and its myriad experiences are her concern. These collected works range in both content and tone from the sacred to the profane, from grief to joy, and the journey both in its language and vision is impressive and courageous. Manoo-Rahming guides the reader through national, regional, and familial history while simultaneously revealing, mourning and celebrating her diverse cultural inheritance." — Sandra Pouchet Paquet, Ph.D., Professor Emerita of English, University of Miami.

*INSTANT MESSAGES by Laura Solomon. Hong Kong and the UK, 23 November 2010. pbk. 168pp. Proverse Prize Joint-Winner (2009). ISBN 978-988-19320-2-0.
www.chineseupress.com/asp/e_Book_card.asp?BookID=2910&Lang=E
— Life is tough for fifteen-year-old computer nerd Olivia Best. Her twin sister Melanie, who used to be Olivia's best friend, has taken to drinking and self-harming. Her father has no job and a string of unpublished romance novels to his name. Olivia's mother has just left Olivia's father for her lesbian yoga teacher, Sue. To top things off, Olivia is being severely bullied by a gang of boys from a neighbouring estate. Together with her trusted ally, a stuffed toy green frog, Olivia attempts to navigate the stormy seas of her existence.
"Hilarious!" "Excellent!" "Its light and ironic touch makes *Instant Messages* a page-turner and gives it substance." — Proverse Prize Judges.

JOCKEY, by Gillian Bickley (when Gillian Workman). Hong Kong. pbk. 64pp. (inc. several original illustrations and facsimilies). Written for young readers. Based on extensive research. Authentic background to the RHKJC. Suitable as a reference for adults interested in the history of the then Royal Hong Kong Jockey Club. Original illustrations. ISBN-10: 962-85570-3-3; ISBN-13: 978-962-85570-3-5.

*A MAGISTRATE'S COURT IN 19TH CENTURY HONG KONG: COURT IN TIME: Court Cases of The Honourable Frederick Stewart, MA, LLD, Founder of Hong Kong Government Education, Head of the Permanent HK Civil Service & Nineteenth Century HK Police Magistrate. Contributing Ed., Gillian Bickley. Contributors: Garry Tallentire, Geoffrey Roper, Timothy Hamlett, Christopher Coghlan, Verner Bickley. Preface by Sir T. L. Yang. Modern Commentary & Background Essays *with* Selected Themed Transcripts. 1st Edition. Hong Kong and the UK, 2005. pbk. 531pp. inc. bibliography, index, notes, w. 56 b/w archival illustrations. ISBN-10: 962-85570-4-1; ISBN-13: 978-962-85570-4-2.
www.chineseupress.com/asp/e_Book_card.asp?BookID=1898&Lang=E
"The contributors have written with insight and understanding ... a most readable book." — Sir T. L. Yang.
"[The] lengthy introduction ... is a masterly and impartial survey." — Bradley Winterton, *Taipei Times.*
Mobibook e-book edition, 2005, revd 2008 with the new title: A Magistrate's Court in Nineteenth Century Hong Kong: Court in Time: the Court Cases Reported in *The China Mail* of The Honourable Frederick Stewart, MA, LLD, Founder of Hong Kong Government Education, Head of the Permanent Hong Kong Civil Service & Nineteenth Century Hong Kong Police Magistrate. Modern Commentary & Background Essays with Selected Themed Transcripts and Modern Photographs of Heritage Buildings of the Magistracy, Prison and Court of Final Appeal.
ISBN-10: 962-85570-7-6; ISBN-13: 978-962-85570-7-3.

*A MAGISTRATE'S COURT IN 19TH CENTURY HONG KONG With additional discussion of "The Opium Ordinance": COURT IN TIME: 2nd ed. Hong Kong and the UK, 2009. pbk. 536pp. inc. bibliography, index, notes, w. 56 b/w archival illustrations. ISBN-13: 978-962-17724-5-9.
www.chineseupress.com/asp/e_Book_card.asp?BookID=2559&Lang=E

*MISHPACHA—FAMILY by Rebecca Tomasis. Hong Kong and the UK, 23 November 2010. pbk. 316pp. inc. Glossary, Author portrait. Proverse Prize Joint-Winner (2009). Supported by the Hong Kong Arts Development Council. ISBN 978-988-19320-1-3.
Mobipocket Ebook (2010) ISBN 978-988-19321-8-1
http://www.chineseupress.com/asp/e_Book_card.asp?BookID=2911&Lang=E
"Passionate. A saga of women seeking identity." — Proverse Prize Judges.
"Outstanding ... I was engrossed. In ... [one] sense the novel deals with a universal issue — the dynamic relationships — between family and state, between cultures, between the varied world-views and motivations possessed by young and old generations. ... *Mishpacha* touches me deeply. ... the author sensually delivers a

Chocolate's Brown Study in the Bag

vividly colourful story-telling how young women negotiate for favourable lifestyles, love, and power while dealing with family difficulties and ... external forces .... Through the young women's painful experiences, *Mishpacha* creates an ambitious thinking place in itself — throughout the book it desperately tries to find out: What on earth has my life got to do with this abstract and symbolic homeland? The novel has a rhythm composed by its black humour and sometimes by light humour. It has its own characteristic literary style. ... It is delightful to see that Hong Kong — an international city upholding freedom of creativity — has eventually became the birthplace of Mishpacha." —Yeeshan Yang, author of *Whispers* and *Moans* and *Palma's Tears*.

*THE MONKEY IN ME: CONFUSION, LOVE AND HOPE UNDER A CHINESE SKY by Caleb Kavon. Hong Kong and the UK, March 2009. ISBN 978-988-17724-4-2.
www.chineseupress.com/asp/e_Book_card.asp?BookID=2521&Lang=E
Mobibook e-book edition (2009). ISBN-13: 978-988-17724-6-6.
24Reader Ebook edition (2010) ISBN 978-988-18479-6-6
"A dynamic exploration of human conscience in today's modern and economically aware Hong Kong. As the recession looms and new cultural trends develop, the book looks forward to the personal and societal changes that must be made. This witty, intelligent and insightful novel works as both an interesting read and a personal quest to find answers." — Stephanie Gaynor, *HK Magazine*, 13 March 2009.
"The main message Kavon communicates is that we live in a desert of low culture and tragic materialism. Humanity is doomed, and our retribution is here in the graceless fall of capitalism. His ode to Hong Kong, in a chapter entitled 'Place of Salvation', is sweet." —Anthony Carlyle, *Time Out*, 27 March 2009.

THE MONKEY IN ME (Chinese translation by Chapman Chen). May 2010.
24Reader Ebook edition (2010) ISBN 978-988-18479-9-7

*MOVING HOUSE AND OTHER POEMS FROM HONG KONG, by Gillian Bickley. Hong Kong and the UK, 2005. pbk. 130pp. w. author's portrait. With a talk given in the English Department Staff Seminar Series at Hong Kong Baptist University. With one CD of all poems read by the author. Preface by Chung Ling.
ISBN-10:962-85570-5-X; ISBN-13: 978-962-85570-5-9.
www.chineseupress.com/asp/e_Book_card.asp?BookID=1992&Lang=E
Mobibook e-book edition (2008) ISBN-10: 962-85570-8-4. ISBN-13: 978-962-85570-8-0.
24Reader Ebook edition (2010) ISBN 978-988-18479-0-4
"The variety of human life and the individual response to life, these are Gillian Bickley's central interests." — Emeritus Professor I. F. Clarke and M. Clarke, UK.

*MOVING HOUSE AND OTHER POEMS FROM HONG KONG, TRANSLATED INTO CHINESE, WITH ADDITIONAL MATERIAL, by Gillian Bickley, Edited by Tony Ming-Tak YIP. Translated by Tony Yip & others. Hong Kong and the UK, June 2008. pbk. 140pp. w. nine b/w photographs & editor's portrait. ISBN-13: 962-988-99668-5-0.
www.chineseupress.com/asp/e_Book_card.asp?BookID=2452&lang=C
24Reader Ebook edition ISBN 978-988-18479-2-8

*OF SYMBOLS MISUSED by Mary-Jane Newton. Foreword by Peter Carpenter. Pbk. 96pp. ISBN: 978-988-19321-5-0
"Mary-Jane Newton's first collection displays boldness of spirit and a buccaneering sense of adventure in its forays with language, matched by energy, a wry sense of humour and humility in the light of the poet's responsibilities, thus making it a joy to read, at turns sensuous and arch in tones and angles." — Peter Carpenter, author of *After the Goldrush* and Chair of the Poetry Society UK.

*A PAINTED MOMENT, by Jennifer Ching. Hong Kong and the UK, March 2010. pbk. w author's portrait (4C). 160pp. Supported by the Hong Kong Arts Development Council. ISBN: 978-988-18905-1-1
www.chineseupress.com/asp/e_Book_card.asp?BookID=2739&lang=E
Mobipocket Ebook edition (2010) ISBN 978-988-18905-6-6
24Reader Ebook edition (2010) ISBN 978-988-19320-7-5
"In the work of Jennifer Ching, Hong Kong has found a new and welcome voice in fiction. And, as one among the many worlds well-chosen words create, *A Painted Moment* is a slender, but significant, novel. In it, the sum total of human experience pushes forward a fraction, inclining immeasurably (if perceptibly) towards the light. There is growth, there is being, there will be a tomorrow. I look forward to Ms Ching's next novel unreservedly." — Stuart Christie.
"The main themes of the novel are self-growth and friendship. Ching has painstakingly illustrated the inevitable moment of self-independence pressing upon us in due time." — Flora Mak, in *Cha: An Asian literary Journal*, Issue 12, September 2010.

*PAINTING THE BORROWED HOUSE: POEMS, by Kate Rogers. Hong Kong and the UK, March 2008. pbk. w. 3 b/w photographs & author's portrait. Preface by Donna Langevin. 68pp. Supported by the Hong Kong Arts Development Council. ISBN-13: 978-988-99668-4-3.

Chocolate's Brown Study in the Bag

www.chineseupress.com/asp/e_Book_card.asp?BookID=2363&Lang=E
Mobibook e-book edition (2009) ISBN 978-988-17724-8-0.
24Reader Ebook edition (2010) ISBN 978-988-18905-2-8
Kate Rogers's first book of poetry. An honest, fresh account by a complex and sensitive woman who has travelled from her native Canada to see and experience new places, people and cultures. — This collection follows her journey as she explores Asia, her life changes and she finally commits herself to remain, learning to live with her choices in a new culture, the "Borrowed House" of the title.

Kate sees beyond the usual dimensions of every day and is open to strange and novel experiences. She reaches out to us through these poems and creates gentle and poignant bonds with her readers. Her perceptions encourage us to be conscious of the archaeology and layered structure of our own lives.

Full of epiphanies, vivid emotion and surprise.

"Ostensibly a voyage through China, Hong Kong and Taiwan, it is really a journey through the emotions." — Bill Purves, author of *China on the Lam*.

"Here is an author in her prime; confident, sure of her craft, and willing to take risks." — Donna Langevin, author of *Improvising in the Dark* and *The Second Language of Birds*.

"These are the poems of a restless muse, sifting and searching a spiritual identity in a foreign land. The Borrowed House is a metaphor with undertones of synecdoche to express the pull and disorientation of the expat with a lust for wandering far from home. . ..   I found myself warming and responding to these poems. . . .there are some very alluring verbal pictures and she is particularly focused on endings that linger in the mind." – Paul Bench, *Word Matters*, Journal of the Society of Teachers of Speech and Drama, Summer 2009, Vol. 59, No. 1, p. 45.

"Kate's poems have a flowing and meditative quality that delves into personal landscapes as well as describing and evoking places and experiences. At times, however, there is a vibrancy about the verse that allows the thrusting modern world, with its HSBC logos and air-conditioned environment to clash with ancient temples and tofu." – Ken Pickering. Professor: The Institute for Arts in Therapy and Education: London, UK. June 2008.

*A PERSONAL JOURNEY THROUGH SKETCHING: THE SKETCHER'S ART, by Errol Patrick Hugh. Hong Kong and the UK, 2009. Introduction by Li Shiqiao. hbk. 96pp. with 100+ original sketches and photographs by the author & author's portrait. 300mm x 215mm x 14mm. w. CD-ROM. ISBN-13: 978-988-18479-1-1.
www.chineseupress.com/asp/e_Book_card.asp?BookID=2657&Lang=E
24Reader Ebook edition (2010) ISBN 978-988-19320-3-7 NYP
Mobibook e-book edition (2010) ISBN 978-988-19321-2-9 NYP
Aims to highlight the artistic energies and the practical wisdom behind the process of the art of sketching, so that readers see the simplicity and magic of complex, on-site, hand-drawn sketches.

Errol Hugh encourages us to put digital cameras aside for a time, to focus our own vision and analytical skills to make a record, in our own way, of what we see and – only after this – to photograph the same scene for comparison and contrast. Using his own pairs of sketches and photographs as examples – with subjects in North America, Hong Kong and Macau as diverse as stilt houses and shining new architecture – he gives us technical tips on how to do it.

"Each sketch is invested with a narrative that links to acts of observation and documentation through engaging afresh with our primary senses. Errol has never lost sight of the fundamental importance of sketching. I take great comfort in seeing the nimble and discerning connections between the eye and the hand in Errol's elegant lines and considered compositions." — Li Shiqiao.

POEMS TO ENJOY (w. sound recording of all poems), Hong Kong Educational Publishing Co. pbk. 3 vols of graded poetry anthologies (kindergarten to adult), with Teachers' Notes. Verner Bickley, editor & anthologiser. ISBN-10: 962-290-018-6; ISBN-13: 978-962-290-018-9; ISBN-10: 962-290-019-4; ISBN-13: 978-962-290-019-6; ISBN-10: 962-290-020-8; ISBN-13: 978-962-290-020-2.

REFRAIN, by Jason S. Polley, Hong Kong and the UK, 23 November 2010. Preface by Kirby Wright. pbk. 88pp. ISBN: 978-988-19321-4-3.
Entered for the inaugural Proverse Prize (2009).
www.chineseupress.com/asp/e_Book_card.asp?BookID=2944 &Lang=E
refrain recounts the author's travels in India as an inexperienced and sensitive young man. The narrative shows wit, intelligence and a facility with words. The style is experimental and literary; and the fascination of the stories told – short stories in verse presenting the anxieties and misfortunes typical of shoestring traveling, and the culture-shock deriving from visiting a very different culture from ones own – carries the careful reader along. A knack for reading this less-than-conventional fast-paced book, which is at once humorous and nightmarish, passionate and detached, is acquired quickly.

"A young man arrives in Delhi with a romanticized view of India, a pocketful of outdated maps, and a money belt begging to be stolen. We experience his battles with disgust and paranoia while moving through a rough and tumble city. Polley takes us along on a ride that feels cinematic, jammed with sensory explosions that rock the sensibilities. The reader is pulled into the text to experience the chaotic, disordered images of India. The stories work as a sprawling dramatic monologue, one that encompasses numerous states and territories. Polley paints on a large canvas and his brush strokes are fresh, memorable, and cutting edge. — Kirby Wright, Honolulu, Hawaii, Author of *Punahou Blues* and *Moloka't Nui Ahina*

*THE RELUCTANT TERRORIST: IN THE PATH OF THE JIZO, by Caleb Kavon. Scheduled 9 March 2011. pbk. ISBN 978-988-19320-8-2.
In this novel, set in contemporary Hong Kong and Japan, with flashbacks to the Second World War, a Japanese businessman takes a deliberately modest revenge against another Japanese family that damaged his own during the Second World War. His surprising act of terrorism is a paradoxical gesture for peace. We meet again characters from Kavon's first novel, "The Monkey in me: Confusion, Love and Hope under a Chinese Sky" (2009).

SEARCHING FOR FREDERICK AND ADVENTURES ALONG THE WAY, by Verner Bickley. Hong Kong, 2001. pbk. 420pp., inc. bibliography, index. w. author's portrait. The story of the book, *The Golden Needle* (the biography of the Founder of Hong Kong Government Education). *With archival and modern photographs.* Supported by the Hong Kong Arts Development Council. ISBN-10:962-8783-20-3; ISBN-13:978-962-8783-20-5.
Narrative of research, with anecdotes, useful addresses and contact information, intermixed with stories and reflections from the author's own life experience, mainly in Asia. *With archival and modern photographs.* "Verner Bickley writes in a mostly light-hearted vein, with a gentle humour." — Sir James Hodge, British Consul General, Hong Kong.

*SIGHTINGS: A COLLECTION OF POETRY, WITH AN ESSAY, "COMMUNICATING POEMS", by Gillian Bickley. Hong Kong and the UK, 2007. pbk. 142pp. w. author's portrait. With a talk given in the English Department Staff Seminar Series at Hong Kong Baptist University. Introduction by Ma Kwai Hung. Preface by Harry Guest. Foreword by Marion Bethel. Supported by the Hong Kong Arts Development Council. ISBN-13: 978-988-99668-1-2.
www.chineseupress.com/asp/e_Book_card.asp?BookID=2264&Lang=E
Mobibook e-book edition (2008). ISBN-13: 978-988-99668-8-1.
24Reader Ebook edition (2010). ISBN 978-988-18479-4-2
"Bickley has made use of everyday life situations and turned them into life lessons. *Sightings* inspires us to slow down and taste the sense of the city." —Ma Kwai Hung, Examiner, Hong Kong Arts Development Council.

SMOKED PEARL: Poems of Hong Kong and Beyond, by Akin Jeje (Akinsola Olufemi Jeje). Preface by Viki Holmes. Hong Kong and the UK, 23 November 2010. pbk. 132pp. Supported by the Hong Kong Arts Development Council. Proverse Prize Semi-finalist (2009). ISBN 978-988-19321-1-2
www.chineseupress.com/asp/e_Book_card.asp?BookID=2943&Lang=E
Smoked Pearl chronicles observations and experiences in Hong Kong, Canada and Africa, and was long-listed for the inaugural international Proverse Prize in 2009.
"A fine collection of free verse; exuberant and thoughtful. Serious, thoughtful and moral; angry, but also loving and compassionate." — Proverse Prize Judges.
"Jeje sees the gleam revealed within the grime: his titular smoked pearl evocative of this interplay of light and dark. For tarnished things must once have been precious, and though Jeje writes of wasted days, he recognises the briefness, 'the glory of the blaze.' ... But for all that Jeje sees — the injustice, the silence and the blame — these darknesses of the human soul are not total: the night ends, hope dawns." — Viki Holmes, author of *miss moon's class.*
"Jeje's gaze swivels from the intensely private to the trans-continentally public, but he remains ever a self-confessed "jack swinger of verbs," offering us luscious, "amorous nouns." Lustillusion. Despairconfusion. This profusion of sights and sounds is tender, scintillating, thought provoking. Priceless." — Xu Xi, author of *Habit of a Foreign Sky* and *Evanescent Isles.*
"Richly imaginative. ... *Smoked Pearl* has a vivid personal touch, characteristically descriptive of the poet's experience and sensations of Hong Kong and beyond his life in this city." — Yeeshan Yang, author of *Whispers and Moans* and *Palma's Tears.*

*SPANKING GOALS AND TOE POKES: FOOTBALL SAYINGS EXPLAINED, by T. J. Martin. Edited by Gillian Bickley. Indexed by Verner Bickley. Preface by John Dykes. Hong Kong and the UK, June 2008. pbk. 106pp. w. 16 b/w illustrations by Jacinta Read & two author's portraits (one with Sir Stanley Matthews). ISBN-13: 978-988-99668-2-9.
www.chineseupress.com/asp/e_Book_card.asp?BookID=2451&Lang=E
Mobibook e-book edition (2008). ISBN-13: 978-988-99668-6-7.
24Reader Ebook edition (2010). ISBN: 978-988-18479-5-9.
Lists and explains more than 800 of the sayings that football commentators use. An enjoyable reference tool which can increase readers' understanding of English language football commentaries and colloquial English expressions in general.

Chocolate's Brown Study in the Bag

"Entertaining.—We have all heard these sayings but now we have easy explanations and some very funny illustrations to call on. A must read football book for fans everywhere." — Paul Truman, Mobipocket website, June 2008.

*THE STEWARTS OF BOURTREEBUSH. Aberdeen, UK, Centre for Scottish Studies, University of Aberdeen, 2003. pbk. 153pp. Extensive documentation of the Scottish family of the Founder of Hong Kong Government Education, Frederick Stewart presenting the perspective of each family member. As such, a reference to writing family history and biography. *With archival photographs and facsimiles of documents, Hong Kong & Scottish subjects.* ISBN-10: 0906265347; ISBN-13: 978-0-906265-34-5.
www.chineseupress.com/asp/e_Book_card.asp?BookID=1787&Lang=E
In a follow-up to her biography of renowned Hong Kong educationalist Frederick Stewart, Dr Gillian Bickley turns the spotlight on his Aberdeenshire, Scotland family. Her archival search, often with her husband Dr Verner Bickley, serves as a model for other researchers engaged in family history.

*TIGHTROPE! – A BOHEMIAN TALE by Olga Walló. Scheduled. Translated from Czech. pbk. c. 276pp. 3 x 4C original illustrations by Monika Abbott. ISBN 13: 978-988-18905-0-4.
www.chineseupress.com/asp/e_Book_card.asp?BookID=2942&Lang=E
Mobipocket Ebook (2010) ISBN 978-988-19321-7-4
An extraordinary, curiously intellectual small girl undertakes the demanding and costly burden of comprehending the world. Her father – a peculiar leftist intellectual, and her mother, a neurotic actress, belonging to an old farming family – are more or less social outcasts, who fight for survival. The situation prevailing in Socialist Eastern Europe in the period after the Second World War – which is both the setting and an inherent part of the fabric of this tale – produces incidents which are funny, cruel, and absurd, eliciting both laughter and compassion. The language of the Czech original is complicated and multileveled, intermixing rural dialect with communist Newspeak, theatre jargon with the lowest "proletarian" argot; and is lifted by the language of philosophical reflections and poetical associations. This English translation of the second volume of Olga Walló's admired novel trilogy based on her own life and times (*Spires of the Holy Spirit*) will certainly attract international readers and increase knowledge of Czech history and culture.
"I believe that all readers, whatever their different cultural experiences, will find in this novel something to identify with, and I hope that, through the personal accounts of the author, they will be able to trace the complex path which our nation travelled not so long ago."— Václav Havel
"Readers who enjoy good prose will find to their liking this imaginatively written and entertaining – but essentially tragic – novel set in the little-known 50s of the last century in Czechoslovakia." — Josef Škvorecký

*WANNABE BACKPACKERS: THE LATIN AMERICAN & KENYAN JOURNEY OF FIVE SPOILED TEENAGERS by Gerald YEUNG. Hong Kong and the UK, 11 March 2009. pbk. 164pp. (w. several b/w pix) ISBN 978-988-17724-2-8.
http://www.chineseupress.com/asp/e_Book_card.asp?BookID=2522&Lang=E
Mobibook e-book edition (2009) ISBN 978-988-17724-7-3.
24Reader Ebook edition (2010) ISBN: 978-988-18479-7-3
The story of five self-confessed "spoiled teenagers" who travel to Latin America and Kenya one summer.

"A Hong Kong story of roughing it the nice way. The story is about the interaction among the five during their 30 days on the road together. 'Some things we found out about each other, we really didn't want to know.'" — Annemarie Evans, *South China Morning Post*.
"Written in diary style, the book conveys the precarious state of a young man poised between a protected childhood and imminent independence as an adult, providing fabulous insight for parents into what's really going on in a teen's mind. Encounters with girls, 'weird' food and clubbing in a foreign language are balanced with budding understanding of the differences of other cultures and appreciation of their beauty. Each of the friends adds their own epilogue summing up the group's collective experience." — *Parents' Journal*, Hong Kong.